NUCLEAR ENERGY IN INDUSTRY

NUCLEAR ENERGY IN INDUSTRY

By

J. G. CROWTHER

PITMAN PUBLISHING CORPORATION
NEW YORK TORONTO LONDON

First published 1956

Printed in Great Britain

PREFACE

BRITAIN CONTAINS ENOUGH COAL to meet the present trends of her consumption for about two centuries. The world contains enough uranium to provide Britain with a share which would enable her to meet her present trends of demand for energy for about two thousand years. Sir John Cockcroft has remarked that within that time scientists will probably have discovered how to control the fusion of the light elements—the kind of reaction which occurs in a hydrogen bomb. When this has been achieved, the supply of energy will be virtually unlimited, for it would then be possible to utilize the enormous quantities of hydrogen in the water of the oceans for the production of power.

Cockcroft has given scientists two thousand years to achieve this supreme discovery. The President of the International Conference on the Peaceful Uses of Atomic Energy, held at Geneva in 1955, the eminent Indian physicist, Dr. Homi J. Bhabha, forecast that the control of the fusion reaction would be discovered within the next twenty years. Within two thousand years, or twenty, the era of unlimited energy is historically very close.

Besides eliminating all shortages of energy which have hindered conventional developments, such as the industrial production of goods and the growth of food, the coming era will see not only the further discovery but the making of basic raw materials. Our descendants will see not the mere working of iron but the synthesis of iron, and of all the other metals and elements which at present mankind, with laborious toil, gratefully digs out of the earth, where it was deposited by Nature, after having been made by her in the cosmos.

Our own age is of a very transitory character, and our struggles with material and economic shortages will seem to the people of the future as crude and pitiful as the stocks and stones of the people of the Old Stone Age seem to us. But we who live today, who can see the future of unlimited power, will have a very hard time in helping to solve the innumerable problems which will bring the new era into being. For the immediate future we shall be very largely occupied with the better utilization of conventional powers of coal, oil and water, and the beginning of the utilization of nuclear energy. We shall be engaged in incessant labour on one problem after another, so that the character of industry and agriculture will change continuously, until our transitory journey to the age of unlimited power is completed, and mankind enters into an era which will be exceedingly different from all that have passed before.

Though we who live today may not ourselves enter that new era of unlimited power, we work in the knowledge that it is coming soon. We pursue our ordinary activities and daily life, while the first rays of an unimaginably brilliant future rise above the horizon. The aim of this book is to give some impression of what is afoot, and how industry looks in the light of nuclear power, and the innumerable directions in which it is already being affected, and will be remodelled. So the reader may be helped to find his way in the new world of nuclear power, and see how industry will be affected, and the directions in which there will be a demand for new products, new trades and new ways of life.

Adjustment to the new situation is not easy. At first the immediate changes in industry will seem rather small and disappointingly slow. But later on we shall suddenly become aware that the whole of industry and life has become permeated with the new ideas and methods, and we shall see these developing all around us at a tremendous rate. The growth of the new industrial revolution will in itself be a kind of chain-reaction. We have the task of persevering with the new ideas and difficult problems at the beginning of the atomic age, when progress may be slow, so that later on, when progress becomes fast, we shall be equipped to obtain the maximum benefit from it.

The term Atomic Energy has come into general use for describing the new source of energy which is being secured from atoms. It is explained in Chapter II that the old source of energy obtained, for example, by the combustion of coal, also comes from atoms, but only in low intensity from their outer part, while the new source of energy comes in high intensity from the entirely different inner part of the atom, the Nucleus. Thus, strictly speaking, the term Nuclear Energy for the new source of power from the nucleus is more exact. Hence in this book Atomic Energy is used for referring to the subject in general terms, but in the description of particular processes the term Nuclear Energy is preferred.

The author is grateful to Mr. P. W. Mummery, who kindly read the manuscript and suggested a number of corrections; to the Directors of Messrs. George Newnes Ltd. and Mr. E. Molloy, General Editor of Messrs. Newnes' Technical Books Department, who made it possible for him to attend the unique International Conference on the Peaceful Uses of Atomic Energy, held at Geneva in 1955; and to Miss Evelyn Drury for courteous assistance in seeing the book through the press.

J. G. C.

CONTENTS

ACKNOWLEDGMENTS

THANKS ARE DUE to the following for their assistance in obtaining or supplying photographs and line drawings for inclusion in this book:

Argonne National Laboratory, U.S.A.; Atomic Energy of Canada Limited; Babcock & Wilcox Ltd.; The British Cotton Industry Research Association; The Brazilian Embassy; Butterworth & Co. (Publishers) Ltd.; Central Office of Information; The English Electric Company Ltd.; General Electric Company Ltd., U.S.A.; G. A. Harvey and Co. (London), Ltd.; The High Commissioners of Canada, New Zealand and South Africa; The Institute of Atomic Information for the Layman; The Institution of Mechanical Engineers; The Radiac Company Inc.; Radiation Laboratory of the University of California; Radiation Research Corporation; Shell Petroleum Ltd.; The Soviet Embassy; Union Carbide International Company; The United Kingdom Atomic Energy Authority; The United Nations Information Centre, London; The U.S. Atomic Energy Commission; The U.S. Information Service of the American Embassy, London; Westinghouse Electric Company Ltd.

CHAPTER I

THE IMPENDING REVOLUTION

MAN HAS EXISTED more than a quarter of a million years, yet, until only about two centuries ago, he had to depend on his own muscles, eked out by contributions from animals, wind and water, for his main source of power.

A man, or woman, working at the limits of human strength can produce only a little more than is necessary for subsistence. Consequently the power required for the arts and constructions of civilization was first obtained by appropriating the small surplus from individuals, the majority of whom lived permanently on the edge of subsistence, and were in fact slaves.

Today, in the most advanced countries the production of energy per head of the population is equal to that of ninety human slaves.

TABLE 1

Source of Energy	*Percentage of Total*
Coal	41·4
Lignite and peat	4·5
Petroleum	26·5
Natural gas	9·3
Water power	1·4
Wood and agricultural products	15·9
Muscle : human and animal	1·0

The effective escape from bondage began in the eighteenth century, with the development of the steam engine. This gave man the possibility of superseding muscles as the chief source of power by utilizing the enormous reserves of energy locked up in coal.

Before James Watt's improved steam-engine, coal made a very small contribution to the world's work, and mineral oil and natural gas were scarcely known. But by 1952 nearly 82 per cent of the world's energy supplies came from these mineral resources, and only 1 per cent from human and animal muscles.

Consumption of energy in 1952 was estimated to be equivalent to that which would be provided by the burning of 3,567 million tons of hard coal. The percentages of this total from various sources are given in Table 1.

This table has several significant features. It shows that mankind has not only changed its main sources of fuel and power but has also come to depend on sources of a fundamentally different character. Before the steam-engine, power and energy were obtained from human beings and animals, and the products of plants, such as wood. These were continually renewed by the processes of growth, drawing their energy directly or indirectly from the sun's rays. Hence the human societies based on them, though hard, were stable. They lasted for thousands of years and gave man the time to solve many difficult problems in the development of civilization.

But our industrial civilization of today is based to the extent of more than 80 per cent on fossil fuels which, so far as we can see at present, cannot be replenished once they are used up. Coal was formed out of trees and plants which grew in a particular period on the earth 250 million years ago. Oil, which is apparently being used up still more quickly, is also supposed to have been formed out of living organisms, though some modern theories ascribe its origin to carbon compounds in the primeval particles out of which the earth was first conglomerated.

Thus, during the last two centuries, while acquiring a vast accession of power from coal, oil and gas, mankind has also exchanged a stable for an unstable energy basis of society. An industrial civilization based primarily on coal, oil and gas cannot go on for long, a few centuries at the most, a mere moment in the long history of man, because the reserves of these fossil fuels are necessarily limited.

Another significant feature of Table 1 is the relatively small contribution from water-power. Even after the huge hydro-electric stations of the first half of the twentieth century had been constructed, the contribution of water-power to the world pool of energy supplies was only 1·4 per cent. The world's potential resources of water-power are not large enough to meet the further demands for energy. Their chief importance is not in their quantity but in their availability and renewability. The technique of harnessing them is thoroughly developed, and can be readily carried out, after the decisions to undertake the development have been made. The complete harnessing of the world's rivers would be one of the quickest ways of making a big addition to energy resources, and it would be of a specially valuable kind, because water-power is a renewable resource. But it would not meet more than a small part of the demand for energy.

In Table 2 the consumption of energy over the period 1860–1954 is shown graphically. The grand total is represented by a fairly

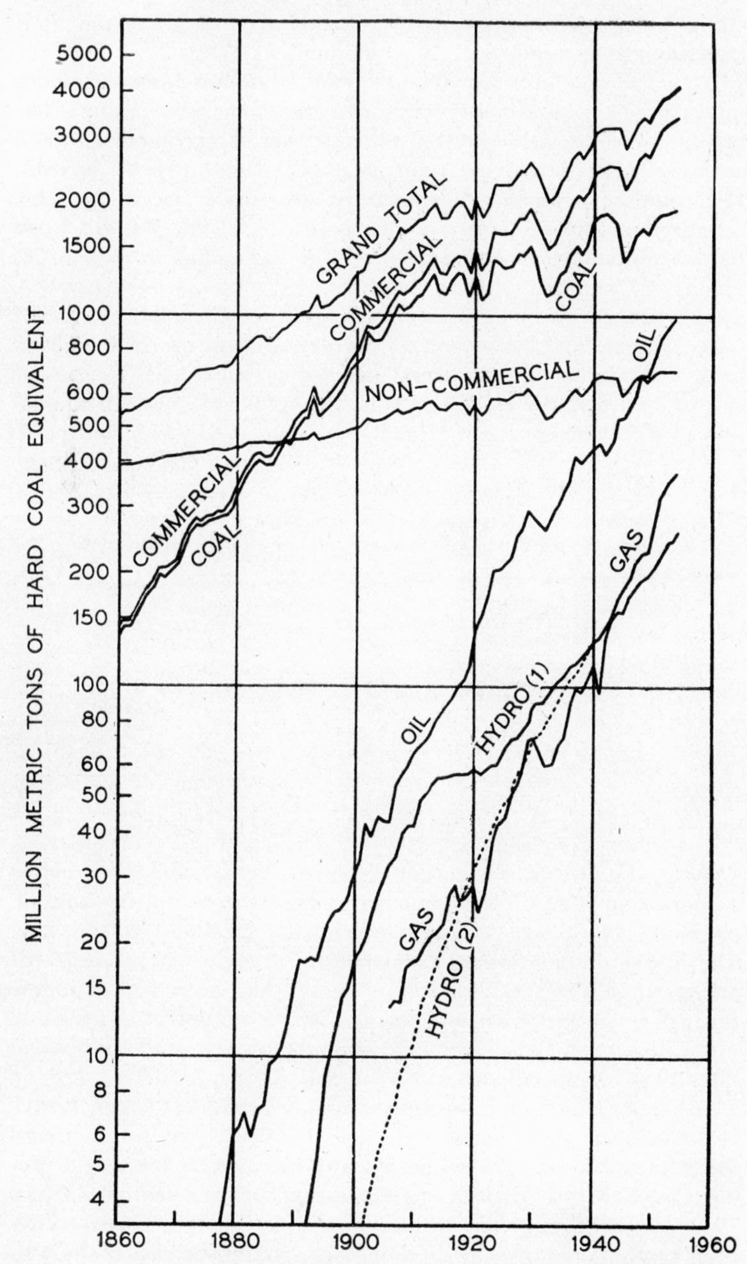

TABLE 2.—WORLD ENERGY SUPPLIES IN TOTAL AND BY SOURCES, 1860–1954.

straight rising line, which means on this kind of graph that it is increasing at a steady rate of compound increment. In fact, the world consumption of energy has for the last hundred years been increasing at a compound rate of 2 per cent per annum. The steadiness of this increase over a long period is very important, and strongly suggests that the total demand will continue to increase at a compound rate of the same order for many years. This Table is reproduced from Conference Paper P/757, " The World's Need for a New Source of Energy ", by E. A. G. Robinson and G. H. Daniel, by permission of the authors.

In 1950 the world production of energy from inanimate sources—coal, oil, gas and water-power—was equivalent to 2,800 million tons of hard coal. If the world demand increases at a compound rate of 2 per cent per annum, then the demand in 1975 will be equivalent to 4,500 million tons of coal.

TABLE 3

TOTAL WORLD DEMAND FOR ENERGY FROM COAL, OIL, GAS AND WATER SOURCES, INCREASING AT A COMPOUND RATE OF 2 PER CENT PER ANNUM

Year	*Total World Demand*
1950	2,800 million tons
1975	4,500 " "
2000	7,400 " "
2025	12,100 " "
2050	19,900 " "

While the total world output of energy has steadily increased at a compound rate of 2 per cent per annum, the output of coal, oil, gas and water-power has not individually increased at this rate. The world output of coal is increasing at only 0·5 per cent per annum, and the total output of energy has been kept up only through much faster rates of increase in the output of oil, gas and water-power, which has been increasing respectively at the compound rates of 4·7 per cent, 6·3 per cent and 3·3 per cent.

Table 4, which is reproduced from Conference Paper P/902, " World Energy Requirements in 1975 and 2000 ", by permission of the United Nations, shows graphically how slowly the world production of coal has risen during the last quarter of a century. Since 1913, the steady increase in total world production of energy has been kept up only through an immensely greater increase in the production of oil and natural gas. By 1953 it depended almost as much

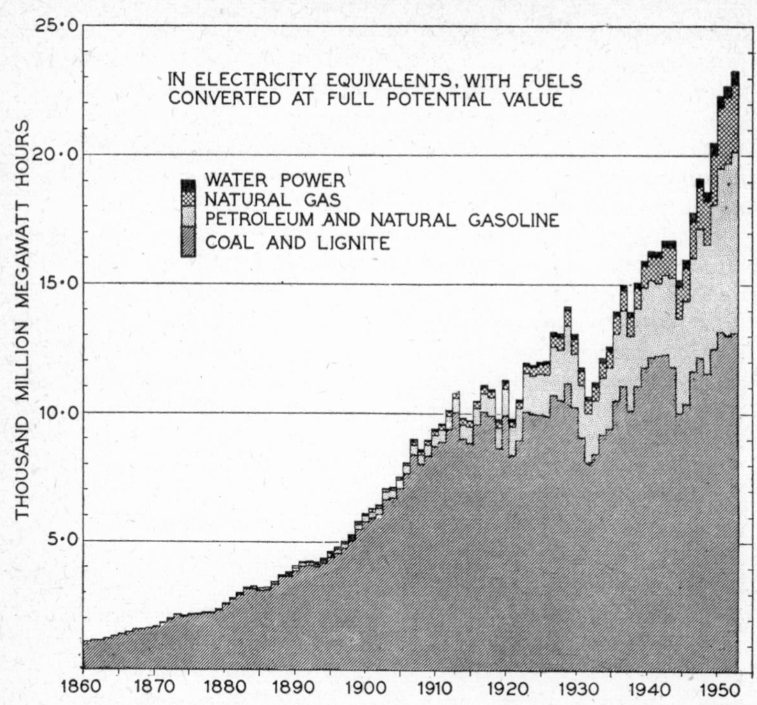

TABLE 4.—WORLD PRODUCTION OF COMMERCIAL SOURCES OF ENERGY, 1860–1953.

on oil and gas as on coal, and within the next five years it will begin to draw more energy from oil and gas than from coal.

Estimates in 1955 of the total world reserves of conventional fuels are given in Table 5.

TABLE 5

WORKABLE WORLD RESERVES IN HARD COAL EQUIVALENTS

Coal and lignite	3,000,000 million tons
Oil and gas	300,000 ,, ,,
Oil shales and tar sands	150,000 ,, ,,
Water-power annual output	2,500 ,, ,,

It will be noted that the estimated reserve of oil and gas is only one-tenth that of coal and lignite, but the compound rate of increase in consumption of oil and gas is at present more than ten times that of coal.

At the 1950 rate of demand, the coal and lignite reserves might last for nearly two thousand years. But in the absence of any fundamentally new source of energy, the demand for coal as fuel will increase rapidly, and as the smaller oil reserve is used up, the conversion of coal into oil will stimulate the demand still more. Under these circumstances, the coal deposits would be exhausted in a few centuries. According to some estimates, the coal reserves might be exhausted within two hundred years.

In addition to their use as fuel, coal, oil and gas will be needed more and more as raw materials for the chemical industry. Already in 1954, 12 per cent of the organic chemicals made in Britain were prepared from petroleum. Not only is the bulk of this production considerable and rising rapidly, but its quality is of special importance, for petroleum provides a particularly large part of the raw materials for the new modern industries of plastics, resins, synthetic fibres, detergents and solvents.

The world's reserves of coal, oil and gas will be needed more and more as a store of raw materials for chemical industry, which should be carefully husbanded as the raw materials of thousands of subtle and valuable products, and not be crudely consumed as fuel.

The slow rate of increase of output of coal is due to technical and social difficulties. As mines get deeper and seams thinner, the coal becomes more difficult to win. As the general standard of living rises, it becomes more and more difficult to persuade men to work in mines.

Thus mankind is turning over to oil and gas, which apparently exist in much smaller quantities, and is consuming them at a very much greater rate of increase than the larger resource of coal.

The world demand for energy in the year 2000, on the lowest estimates, will be not less than the equivalent of 7,400 million tons of coal. According to Guyol, it will more probably be nearer 20,000 million tons of coal-equivalent. Yet by the year 2000 the production of coal itself, at a compound increase of 0·5 per cent per annum, will have risen to only 2,000 million tons. Thus the equivalent of at least 5,400 million tons would have to be found from other sources, such as oil, gas and water. It is estimated that by the year 2000 the output of water-power may have been increased from the present annual output of an equivalent of 200 million tons of coal to perhaps 1,000 million tons, but this would still leave a minimum deficiency of 4,400 million tons coal-equivalent. If this were met by a vastly increased consumption of oil, then this apparently much smaller reserve of energy would, according to present estimates of its size and the minimum rate of demand as forecast for the year 2000, be used up by the year 2070.

Many experts forecast higher rates of increase of consumption than those quoted here, and consequently take a still more pessimistic view of the situation. However the figures are looked at, our industrial civilization, according to our present knowledge of resources, cannot continue to be based mainly on coal and oil for more than a few decades, or centuries at the most.

Yet it should never be forgotten that revolutionary discoveries may occur even in the conventional industries of coal and oil. If the energy of coal could be secured on a large scale by gasification, or conversion into oil, of the seams underground, so that mining of solid coal with its technical and social difficulties is eliminated, the rate of increase of production of energy from coal might be greatly accelerated.

It is not inconceivable that the reserves of oil in the earth will prove to be of an altogether higher order than has yet been discovered. The most recent theories of the origin of the earth suppose that it has been formed by the accretion of small particles of dust in the regions near the sun. These particles consisted mainly of iron and nickel, with traces of ice, and compounds of carbon and hydrogen, and some other substances. As the particles compacted together through aeons of time, forming a larger and larger sphere, the iron and nickel formed the present core of the earth, while the ice melted into water, and was gradually exuded to the surface. It is now believed that the water of our present oceans came originally from the inside of the earth, and not from condensation of clouds of primeval steam outside the earth. In a similar way, it may be that oil has been formed from the compounds of carbon and hydrogen in the original particles, and has gradually been exuded from the centre of the earth to those places near the surface where it is now found. Moreover, this process is still going on, so that vast quantities of hydrocarbons in the deeper layers of the outer jacket of the earth are still making their way towards the surface. In spite of the relatively small reserves of oil yet located, undiscovered oceans of oil may exist deep down in the pores of the earth.

At present these ideas are only a warning against dogmatism. An important concrete factor which has already had a conspicuous effect is the improvement in the efficiency in the use of fuel. In 1920 the average efficiency of thermo-electric power plants was 9 per cent. This was raised to 24 per cent by 1952, and the efficiency of a large modern plant is now 30 per cent. The replacement of steam by Diesel locomotives on railways enables three times as much energy for transport to be obtained from equivalent quantities of fuel consumed. The general adoption of Diesel locomotives since 1929 has led to an immense increase in the efficiency of the use of fuel on the United States railways. Nevertheless, in spite of these engineering triumphs, the total world demand for fuel has continued obstinately to increase at the compound annual rate of 2 per cent. The improvements in the efficiency of power plants during the last quarter of a century have been remarkable, but they cannot be carried very much further, as each succeeding unit gain in efficiency becomes harder to win, and finally the engineer is halted by the laws of thermodynamics and the properties of materials.

In *A Programme of Nuclear Power* it is stated that the efficiency of steam power stations in the British public electricity supply system has improved according to the figures given in Table 6.

TABLE 6

Year	*Pounds Weight of Coal used per Unit generated*
1925	2·43
1935	1·54
1945	1·42
1950	1·37
1954	1·26

Higher efficiency can make a brilliant contribution to the better use of coal, but it cannot solve the conventional fuel problem. Coal, oil and natural gas, our main sources of energy today, cannot continue to bear the brunt of the increasing world demand for energy for more than a few decades. The situation would soon be impossible, even on conservative estimates of the rate of increase of energy demand, in which countries are supposed to remain at their present relative standards.

Today, the consumption of energy per head of the population in the United States is about ten times that of India. If the 400 million people of India were provided with as much energy per head as the people of the United States this would require the doubling of the present world production of energy, and if this extra energy were obtained from Indian coal alone, the known coal reserves of that country would be exhausted in less than ten years. There is not enough coal, oil, gas and water-power in India to provide the means by which the Indian standard of living could be raised to that which already exists in the United States. According to Bhabha, India obtains 80 per cent of her energy by burning 224 million tons of dung every year. This ought to be used as manure to increase the crops of food, which is already in short supply.

The raising of standards to uniform levels throughout the world would involve immense increases in energy requirements. For instance, agriculture, in which more than 80 per cent of the world's workers are engaged, still, in 1952, derived four-fifths of the energy used in its operations from human and animal muscles. Of this, about three-fifths was provided by draft animals and two-fifths by human labour. The one-fifth not derived from animate resources was provided mainly by oil-driven tractors.

If the energy consumption per person could be raised immediately to the American standard, and derived from coal, oil, gas and water-power, the present world production of these resources would have to be multiplied by 5½ times, that is, their coal-equivalent would have to be raised to about 20,000 million tons per annum. Even if the population of the world remained stationary, the world-reserves of coal, if used at this rate, would last only 150 years.

But the population of the world does not remain stationary. At the beginning of the Christian era it was probably about 300 million. It rose slowly until the beginning of the industrial revolution about 1750, when it was probably about 500 million. Since then it has risen rapidly. In 1954 it was about 2,500 million, and increasing at the rate of 10 per cent per decade. Experts variously estimate the world population in the year 2000 from 3,200 to 5,000 million.

The quantity of energy required to bring the standard of the world population of A.D. 2000 up to that of the United States in 1950 would be vast. But the standard in the United States continues to rise swiftly. To bring the energy standard of all the people of the world in A.D. 2000 up to the standard of the United States in A.D. 2000 would call for still more enormous increases.

It is evident that the provision of energy from conventional sources to meet the prospective world demand in the year A.D. 2000 is virtually impossible. The latest estimates given by J. C. Johnson at the International Conference on the Peaceful Uses of Atomic Energy show, however, that the world is rich in uranium. Johnson stated that at least one million tons of uranium can be mined at a reasonable price, and very much larger quantities exist, but in conditions which would at present be expensive to work. There are at least equal quantities of thorium, perhaps three times as much. One million tons of uranium is equivalent to 10,000 to 1,000,000 million tons of coal, according to the efficiency with which it is used. The earth contains much more energy in the form of uranium than in the form of coal. Thus even if mankind depended only on coal and uranium, the supplies should last for two thousand years. And within that period, the controlled release of nuclear energy from the fusion of hydrogen atoms, which occurs uncontrolled in the hydrogen bomb, should be discovered. Nature found the solution thousands of millions of years ago, for the enormous and steady outpouring of energy from the sun, which has continued undiminished for countless ages, is derived from a controlled hydrogen fusion reaction proceeding in its core. Man's aim now is to make his own miniature suns. Sir John Cockcroft has forecast that the controlled hydrogen fusion reaction will be discovered within two thousand years, before coal and uranium are exhausted. Dr. Bhabha forecast in his presidential address to the International Conference on the Peaceful Uses of Atomic Energy that it would be discovered within twenty years.

As the supply of ordinary and heavy hydrogen in the water of the oceans is, according to industrial measures, virtually limitless, the discovery of the controlled fusion reaction would bring mankind within sight of virtually unlimited supplies of energy.

Nevertheless, the immediate energy-situation in the world at large is difficult, and in Britain it is also particularly urgent. Britain contains the biggest concentration of industry in the world. She is dependent on the exports of the products of this industry for a major part of her food and raw materials. A serious shortage of fuel would cause her industry to contract and perhaps the consequent decline in exports might upset the delicate balance of her world trade, so that most of her imports would be cut off. The sustentation and increase of her fuel supplies are therefore of cardinal importance.

Yet the production of her major native fuel, deep-mined coal, fell from 289 million tons in 1913 to 175 million tons in 1945. In spite of large new capital investment in equipment, the construction of new pits and the improvement of working conditions, the output has been restored to only 214 million tons, and the increased expenditure and effort are barely enabling the present output to be maintained.

During the Second World War, Britain lost much of her overseas investments and accumulated new debts. In order to meet these liabilities and at the same time find vast sums for military purposes and raised standards of living, the production of home industry, and the exports of manufactured goods, had to be greatly increased. This in turn increased the industrial demand for fuel, which has been met by improved efficiency, but also by a spectacular increase in the imports of oil, which rose from 2 million tons in 1946 to 21 million tons in 1954, and the continued rationing of the householder. Finally, Britain has begun to import coal on a large scale at a high price. In 1954–55 she imported 7 million tons at a price of £7 per ton. Coal was even brought to Newcastle, and by the end of 1955 she was importing coal at the rate of one million tons per month.

Apart from the expense of the imported fuel, which has to be met by still bigger exports of goods, the whole economy of the country becomes more and more delicately balanced. A sudden cessation of the new big imports of oil due, for example, to changes in the Middle East, would give the national economy a severe blow. The inherent stability of the country is reduced.

The fundamental difficulties in Britain's economic situation are reflected in her balance of payments problem. This cannot be solved securely as long as her increasing needs for energy are met by increasing imports of oil and coal. Unless she can find another source of energy, not so limited as her own resources of coal, or so uncertain as oil, the expansion of her industry and raising of her standard of life cannot proceed on a secure basis. Fortunately, as Sir John Cockcroft has remarked, " for us atomic power has come just in time ". Britain has begun her development of atomic energy with a brilliance inspired in part by a sense of national danger.

In 1945 there were no nuclear energy installations in this country. Within ten years a big nuclear energy organization has been created, by scientific and technical efforts more intense even than those during the Second World War. A nuclear power plant for delivering more than 50,000 kilowatts of electricity to the National Grid has been designed and is in an advanced stage of construction.

It is evident that the industrialization based primarily on coal, oil and gas must be a brief period in the history of mankind because the deposits and reserves of these substances in the earth are limited, and are being consumed quickly. We have already started on a new industrial revolution based on a new source of energy, which will influence every aspect of industry, and of human life.

While the prospective extent of the new revolution cannot be exaggerated, and for this reason cannot be given too much thoughtful attention, it should be realized that the immediate British expenditure involved will not be relatively large in the economic sense. The British Government has embarked on a ten-year plan of atomic power development, involving an expenditure of £300,000,000, or about £30,000,000 per annum. The total output of goods and services in Britain in 1954 was valued at £12,214,000,000. The proposed expenditure of £30,000,000 per annum is less than 0·25 per cent of the value of the national output of goods and services.

But the relatively small volume of the initial economic results of the revolution should not divert attention from its ultimate economic effects. It is estimated that by 1975 British atomic exports will be £300 million per annum, and the home market will be about the same size. Those industrial organizations which prepare themselves to enter the new field will find that more and more of the industrial work of the future will come to them, and it is very probable that the rate of increase in business will be much greater than that envisaged in the British Government's ten-year programme.

In Britain various organizations have joined together in order to meet the new demand. The English Electric Company, which incorporates many firms, including certain of those founded by Robert Stephenson, the Siemens brothers, Marconi, and Napier, has formed a consortium with Babcock & Wilcox Ltd., the makers of steam generating plant for power stations, who have supplied more than half the boilers in British power stations; and Taylor Woodrow Ltd., the constructional firm who have built London Airport and many other big civil engineering works. This consortium has announced that it is prepared to construct and equip under a single contract complete atomic power stations in any part of the world.

The Associated Electrical Industries and John Thompson group of companies, the G.E.C.–Simon Carves Atomic Energy Group, and the Nuclear Power Plant Company, including C. A. Parsons & Co., Head Wrightson & Co., Sir Robert McAlpine & Sons, Whessoe, and other firms, have also formed a consortium for supplying industrial demands arising from the development of nuclear energy. Vickers Ltd., Rolls Royce Ltd., and Foster Wheeler Ltd. have formed a company named Vickers Nuclear Engineering Ltd. for the development of atomic energy to marine and submarine propulsion.

Similar consortiums have been formed in the United States.

More than £5,000,000,000 has already been spent in the United States on atomic energy, nearly the whole of this vast sum for primarily military applications. The budget of the U.S. Atomic Energy Commission for the year ending June 1953 was $4,144,000,000, or about £1,500,000,000. About 3 per cent of the total building expenditure of the United States was being absorbed in atomic energy constructions, involving 2 per cent of the whole constructive industry of the country, and about 5 per cent of its entire engineering and scientific personnel. The American nuclear energy industry consumes about as much electricity as the total output of the British Central Electricity Authority, that is, about 20,000,000 kilowatts. Nearly all of this energy is at present carried away from the plants by cooling water, and wasted.

Many of the U.S. Atomic Energy Commission's projects are operated on its behalf by industrial corporations. The Union Carbide and Carbon Corporation operates the Gaseous Diffusion

Plant, the Electro-magnetic Separation Plant, and the National Laboratory, all at Oak Ridge, Tennessee. The new city of Oak Ridge, built for the accommodation of workers in these plants, already has a population of 32,000.

The Corporation is building a new gaseous diffusion plant at Paducah, Kentucky, at a cost of about $1,000,000,000.

The nuclear power plant of the U.S. submarine *Nautilus* was constructed by the Westinghouse Electric Corporation, and the ship was built in the yards of the General Dynamics Corporation.

Up to the present time, the total U.S. expenditure on nuclear energy has been about thirty times that of Britain. Yet by the end of 1955, Britain was in the lead in the construction of the first large-scale nuclear power plant. This was due to the American preoccupation with the military applications of nuclear energy, and to the less urgent pressure in that country to find ways of supplementing her reserves of coal, which are ten times greater per head than in Britain, and her big reserves of water-power not yet harnessed.

As the United States can still greatly expand her output of cheap power from coal and water, her investors are relatively less interested in the new nuclear power. America has tended to pursue a long-range plan of fundamental engineering research, rather than to start immediately on the construction of large-scale industrial nuclear power plants. Her policy in nuclear power development in 1955 has resemblances to that of Britain in jet engine development in 1945. Ten years later, this paid high dividends through superior performance. It is possible that the present American advanced research policy in nuclear engineering will pay high dividends in 1965 by producing plant of superior efficiency.

On the other hand, there is no complete alternative to the experience gained from constructing and using large industrial nuclear power plants now. This will give information, for example, on reliability of operation under normal industrial conditions, which could not be gained in any other way.

The increasing fuel shortage has forced the earlier entry into the production of industrial nuclear power.

According to *A Programme of Nuclear Power*, the cost of electricity from the first commercial nuclear power stations will be about 0·6 of a penny per unit. This is about the same as the probable cost of electricity from new coal-fired power stations, using the increasingly expensive British coal. The figure depends on an estimate, which has been disputed, of the value of plutonium as a by-product of the first nuclear power stations. Even without credit for the plutonium, Jukes has estimated that the price might be

0·76*d.* per unit. But, as Bronowski has remarked, the price of energy in an industrial country such as Britain is not of primary importance, for, on the average, the energy consumed in making manufactured goods is only about 4 per cent of their cost.

In the U.S.S.R., with its different forms of industrial organization, parallel developments have taken place. The Soviet Union announced in August 1955 that it is designing and will manufacture 2,000-kilowatt thermal nuclear piles and 25-million electron-volt particle-accelerating cyclotrons for Poland, Czechoslovakia, Rumania, Hungary, Bulgaria and the German Democratic Republic. For China the U.S.S.R. is designing and manufacturing an experimental 6,500-kilowatt thermal nuclear pile and a 25-million electron-volt cyclotron, and the Soviet Government has stated that it is willing to consider extending the number of countries which it could assist in the peaceful uses of atomic energy.

Thus new combinations of industrial organizations have been formed in the leading industrial countries of the world, for carrying out big contracts, for export as well as home consumption.

The heavy engineering projects of nuclear power are already of considerable economic magnitude, and more and more of the national wealth will be invested in them. But in addition to the large new quantity of industrial demand, there will also be a new quality of demand. Thousands of new kinds of materials and instruments have already been produced for nuclear purposes. The 1954 *Nucleonics Manufacturers' Index* contains a list of 1,300 firms providing supplies for the nuclear energy industry. Its Buyers' Guide contains 66 pages of items of equipment, classified under 700 main types of instruments and materials.

The production of these new materials and instruments form new industries. But this is not the limit of their value and influence. The new materials and instruments brought into existence for use in connection with nuclear energy will be found to have uses in old industries, and the demand for them will be much greater than that from the nuclear industry alone. For instance, the demand for Geiger counters, developed in the study of nuclear physics, is at present larger in the prospecting industry for petroleum than in the nuclear energy industry itself.

The new technique of nuclear industry will penetrate and influence thinking in the old industries. It is therefore to the advantage of all industrialists, even those whose industry at first sight seems to have nothing to do with nuclear energy, to familiarize themselves with its ideas and techniques, so that they can adopt those which may improve their own processes.

CHAPTER II

WHAT IS NUCLEAR ENERGY?

ENERGY IS THE CAPACITY for doing work. It is a concept which was brought forth by the first industrial revolution. The invention of the steam-engine produced a machine which was capable of doing work on an entirely new scale. Hitherto, work had been done by men or horses, with a little assistance from water-wheels and windmills. All men, and all horses, were approximately equal to the rest of their kind in their capacity of doing mechanical work, and the idea of a man-power, or a horse-power, was known to everyone from experience. More accurate units were not needed. Nor were these rough-and-ready units large enough to make exact knowledge of their size very important. The introduction of the steam-engine changed this situation, for it could produce a large power which was not limited by nature like the amount of work which can be done by a man or a horse. The commercial value of the steam engine as a doer of work could not be assessed without an accurate measure of its performance. It was for this reason that James Watt defined the horse-power, in order to make precise measurements of the amount of work his engines could do, and thus fix an appropriate price on them.

The modern conception of energy is the scientific principle which has been derived from the measurement and analysis of steam-engine performance initiated by Watt. After his time it became more and more customary to interpret all actions in material nature as analogous to engines, and, like them, obeying the laws of energy.

Finally, in 1905, Einstein demonstrated that matter itself is a form of energy. Any system which emits energy loses mass in exact proportion to the amount of energy emitted. This was suspected thirty years before Einstein, but the early attempts to prove it failed, because the loss of mass in the energy-producing processes then known, such, for example, as the burning of coal, were far too small to be detected by the available instruments.

After the discovery of radioactivity in 1896, energy-emitting processes were found, such as the spontaneous disintegration of atoms of radium, in which the emission of energy is so large that the loss of mass associated with it is big enough to be detectable by experimental means.

One of the most fundamental discoveries of Pierre and Marie Curie was that radioactivity is a property of the atom, and is not generated by reactions between different substances, like the heat generated when carbon burns in oxygen. They proved, too, that the amount of energy associated with the atom was enormous.

It was evident that the atom concealed hitherto unimagined wonders, and as early as 1902 Rutherford, with his singular genius, announced that he proposed to use the phenomena of radioactivity to force the atom to reveal its structure, and show how it performed its amazing feats of energy-emission. Within nine years he and his pupils discovered the secret of atomic structure, which at once explained why the losses of mass in conventional processes of energy-production, such as the burning of coal, were not detectable by available methods of weighing.

Rutherford proved that the atom consists of a small heavy nucleus, containing nearly all of its mass. Around the nucleus are a number of very light electrons circulating in a pattern which is characteristic for each particular kind of atom, and is determined by the size of the electric charge on the nucleus. Consequently, all nuclei with the same charge have the same pattern of attendant electrons, even though they may be of slightly different masses. Atoms with different nuclear masses but the same chemical properties are called isotopes, because they are all in the same place in the table of the elements, arranged according to their chemical properties.

When two atoms, such as carbon and oxygen, combine together in an ordinary chemical process, such as combustion in a boiler furnace, their respective patterns of attendant electrons are rearranged together in one joined pattern. Within this joint pattern their respective heavy nuclei are imprisoned, together but individually quite unchanged, like two independent worms rolled up in spherical balls within one cocoon.

In chemical reactions such as burning, the changes in the atoms as a whole are confined entirely to their outer gossamer patterns of electrons. They are of such a delicate nature that the energy emissions due to them are small, and consequently the emission of energy in such a process as coal-burning is relatively mild.

Rutherford showed that radioactivity had nothing to do with the outer electrons of an atom, but was entirely due to changes in its nucleus. It was fundamentally different from the changes which occur in chemical reactions, such as combustion.

As the nucleus of the atom is relatively both very heavy and very small, in comparison with electrons, changes in it are of an altogether more intense nature than those in the outer electron pattern.

In fact, a change in the nucleus of an atom involves millions of times as much energy as a change in the outer cloud of electrons. Thus a process in which the nuclei of atoms react together is capable of producing energy with millions of times the intensity in which it is released in a coal-fire, in which atoms of carbon and oxygen react together without their respective nuclei being affected at all.

After proving the nuclear theory of the atom, Rutherford set out to explore the nucleus. He tried to disintegrate it, in order to discover its structure, and succeeded in 1919. Then, in 1932, the young workers in his laboratory made two more major discoveries. J. Chadwick discovered the neutron, whose existence and properties Rutherford had forecast in 1920. This particle has no electric charge, and consequently is not repelled by the electric charge on the nucleus, so it penetrates and changes the nuclei of atoms with exceptional ease.

A few weeks after Chadwick's discovery of the neutron J. D. Cockcroft and E. T. S. Walton showed that nuclei could be split and changed by particles accelerated in a strong electric field. They bombarded atoms of lithium with protons, which are the nuclei of atoms of hydrogen, and showed that they combined together to form two atoms of helium, accompanied by a large release of energy. Measurement showed that the amount of energy released was exactly equivalent to the difference in mass between the two helium atoms on the one hand, and the hydrogen and lithium atom on the other. This experiment was of great interest from several points of view. It showed that nuclear reactions could be produced by man-made machinery on an engineering scale, it gave the first direct experimental proof of Einstein's famous equation of mass and energy, and it furnished a nuclear reaction which has probably been used in one of the types of fusion, or hydrogen bombs. Cockcroft became the director of the Atomic Energy Research Establishment at Harwell, where his combination of abilities has made him one of the founders of nuclear engineering, and one of the most significant figures in the nuclear age.

Shortly after the discovery of the neutron, Ivanenko and Heisenberg independently suggested that the nuclei of atoms consist of combinations of neutrons and protons. This subsequently helped to explain why several neutrons appear when a heavy nucleus is split in the process of fission.

E. Fermi showed that the neutron was peculiarly effective in penetrating atomic nuclei, and producing many different kinds of nuclear changes.

The physicists had now discovered how to make nuclear changes, but they still had no knowledge of how these could be utilized to release nuclear energy on a practical scale.

In 1935 F. Joliot-Curie in his address on receiving a Nobel prize referred to the conception of a nuclear chain-reaction, by which one nuclear reaction sets off others, in the same way that reactions between carbon and oxygen atoms spread through an ordinary fire. Such a nuclear chain-reaction might, he suggested, release nuclear energy on a large scale.

But there was no hint of how such a nuclear chain-reaction could be produced until the unforeseen discovery of uranium fission by Hahn and Strassmann in 1938. Hahn, a former pupil of Rutherford, discovered that when uranium is bombarded with neutrons, its very big heavy nuclei are liable to split into two approximately equal parts, with the emission of an enormous amount of energy. The sum of the masses of the parts is a good deal less than the mass of the original uranium nucleus, and it is this lost mass, which is equal to the energy previously used in binding together the various parts of the uranium nucleus, which reappears as energy of motion in the flying fragments.

As there was previous evidence that atomic nuclei are built up out of protons and neutrons, it seemed possible that when a neutron caused fission in a uranium nucleus, besides the two big fragments, there might also be two or three neutrons, thrown out as specks of nuclear debris or dust from the break-up. Several physicists at once looked for these neutrons, for if they were in fact produced, each might be able to make a fresh uranium fission, thus producing a branching multiplication of fissions, and a vast release of nuclear energy. Joliot-Curie and his colleagues were the first to publish evidence of the release of several neutrons at each fission, and hence of the possibility of a nuclear chain-reaction. The process of fission is shown in Fig. 1.

The basic idea of the release of nuclear energy is extremely simple. It consists of placing suitable atomic nuclei near to each other, so that a chain-reaction grows among them, producing a total of new nuclei whose mass is less than that of the original nuclei. The new nuclei move with an energy which is equal to the mass which has disappeared during the change.

While the principle is simple, its application in practice has demanded a tremendous extension of science. The release of energy from coal by burning requires only a knowledge of the data of chemistry, which have been gradually accumulated during several centuries. But the existence of the atomic nucleus was not known until 1911, and not much exact data about atomic nuclei had been accumulated by 1939, when the release of neutrons during uranium

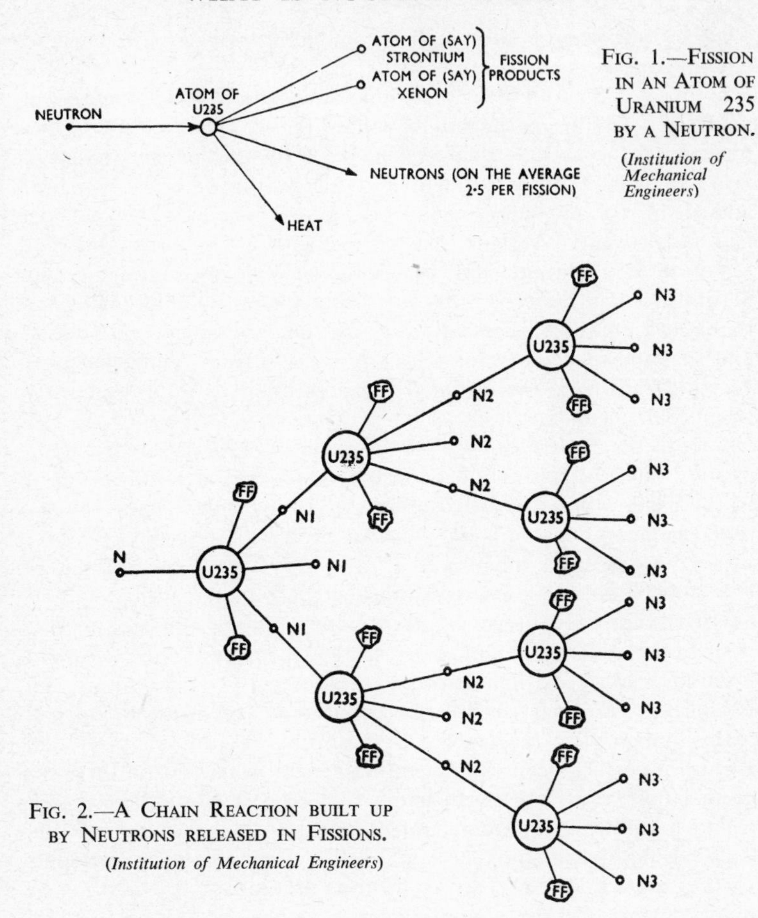

Fig. 1.—Fission in an Atom of Uranium 235 by a Neutron.

(Institution of Mechanical Engineers)

Fig. 2.—A Chain Reaction built up by Neutrons released in Fissions.

(Institution of Mechanical Engineers)

fission suggested that a nuclear chain-reaction might be possible. Fig. 2 illustrates this process diagrammatically.

Figs. 1 and 2, and Fig. 8 on p. 27 are reproduced, by permission of the Council of the Institution of Mechanical Engineers, from the James Clayton Lecture on " Nuclear Reactors and Power Production " by Sir Christopher Hinton, *Proc. Mech. E.*, 1954, vol. 168, p. 55.

Though the idea of releasing nuclear energy is simple in principle, carrying it out in practice is very difficult. This arises from the finer features of atoms. In the rough, they have the same general structure, with a single nucleus and attendant electrons; but in detail they have an immense variety of minute differences, which can be explained only by very abstract mathematical theories.

The arrangement of atomic nuclei so that a steady energy-releasing reaction arose among them involved an immense amount of detailed experimental measurement of atomic data, and abstract theoretical analysis. All this pertained to a new region of experience: the nucleus of the atom. Engineers and scientists took two hundred years to master by experiment and theory the properties of coal and steam for the development of the steam-engine. They have had only twenty years to master the entirely new and different region inside the atom, upon which the utilization of nuclear power depends. It is therefore not surprising that this achievement has required a unique concentration of scientific and engineering effort, and that the machinery for releasing energy from atomic nuclei is very different from the ordinary furnaces used for releasing energy from coal, oil or gas.

So far the controlled release of nuclear energy has depended entirely on the exploitation of uranium, the only substance found in the earth which is easily subject to fission. As happens with other elements, uranium has its own peculiar properties, some of which pose special difficulties.

Natural uranium consists almost entirely of a mixture of two isotopes, that is, two types of atoms with the same chemical properties, but slightly different masses. They are uranium 238 and uranium 235. The light isotope uranium 235 is present in the proportion of 1 part in 140, and it is only this isotope which is easily fissile. The reason why one isotope has this property and the other not has been explained in a general way, and on the basis of the theory forecasts were made that other kinds of nuclei, not found naturally in the earth, might also be subject to easy fission. This has been brilliantly proved by the creation of new elements such as plutonium, and the new isotope uranium 233, which can be made out of thorium. Both of these are subject to fission, and through this have great significance for the future development of nuclear power.

Natural uranium contains easily fissile uranium 235 in a very dilute form. Besides this, the uranium 238 which constitutes the bulk is not neutral to neutrons; it absorbs them strongly. Hence a free neutron in a lump of natural uranium has reduced chances of producing fissions for two reasons, there are relatively so few uranium 235 atoms, and the free neutron itself is liable to be captured by the far more plentiful uranium 238 atoms. For these reasons, a chain-reaction of fissions will not develop spontaneously in a lump of pure natural uranium.

Evidently, one way of making the chain-reaction sustainable is to remove the uranium 238 from the uranium 235. The properties

FIG. 3.—GASEOUS DIFFUSION PLANT, OAK RIDGE, TENNESSEE, U.S.A., WHERE URANIUM 235 AND URANIUM 238 ARE SEPARATED.

(*Union Carbide International Company*)

FIG. 4.—A CONTROL DECK IN THE UNITED KINGDOM ATOMIC ENERGY AUTHORITY'S GASEOUS DIFFUSION PLANT AT CAPENHURST.

(Reproduced from " Britain's Atomic Factories " by permission of the Controller, H.M. Stationery Office. Crown copyright reserved)

of uranium are such that this is extremely difficult, but possible. Uranium combines with fluorine to form the gas uranium hexafluoride. Like most fluorine compounds, this gas is extremely corrosive and difficult to deal with. Its molecules are of two kinds, those containing uranium 238 and those containing uranium 235. As the former are slightly heavier than the latter, they tend to be left behind when the gas diffuses through a porous membrane. By re-cycling the gas through such membranes, the molecules containing uranium 238 can gradually be extracted, so that purer and purer uranium 235 is obtained.

As the difference in mass of uranium 235 and uranium 238 is small, the gas must be re-cycled millions of times, entailing an enormous plant with thousands of miles of pipes and thousands of pumps. The making of fine porous membranes which will resist the highly corrosive hexafluoride gas is technically very difficult. In addition to all this, the uranium working material is radioactive, causing danger to health.

Gaseous diffusion plants are enormous in scale, and require the solution of many new metallurgical problems. They are made entirely automatic in operation, because of the immense number of repetitions of processes and the requirements of safety. They present the most vivid and awe-inspiring examples of the automatic factory, huge complicated plants operating with scarcely a soul about. The gaseous diffusion plant at Oak Ridge, Tennessee, shown in Fig. 3, consists of one building, about 400 feet wide and one mile long.

New plastics, such as fluorothene, which resist corrosion by uranium hexafluoride are used in pumps and piping. The porous barrier must be thin and yet strong, and its pores must have a diameter of about one ten-thousandth of an inch. The thousands of pumps require a large amount of electric power to drive them, and the complete automatic control system, including continuous sampling of the gas by mass-spectrograph, is carried out electrically. Fig. 4 shows this type of plant at the United Kingdom Atomic Energy Authority's establishment at Capenhurst.

The percentage of uranium 235 in uranium can be raised until the metal consists of almost pure uranium 235. In a spherical lump of such material a chain-reaction will develop if the size is big enough to ensure that sufficient neutrons moving inside have the opportunity of causing fissions before they escape through the outer surface. Unless the lump is larger than this critical size, a chain-reaction will not be sustained in it. The several neutrons released in a fission have a speed of about 15,000 kilometres per second, and have to travel only a few centimetres in pure uranium

FIG. 5.—THE FERMI PILE CONSTRUCTED IN A SQUASH-COURT AT THE UNIVERSITY OF CHICAGO. IT PRODUCED THE FIRST ARTIFICIAL NUCLEAR CHAIN REACTION ON DECEMBER 2ND, 1942.

(Argonne National Laboratory)

235 before starting a fresh fission, so the chain-reaction can develop at an enormous rate.

This is the principle of the fast reactor. The critical size necessary for the chain-reaction to develop in pure uranium 235 is quite small. An atomic bomb is a completely uncontrolled type of fast reactor, and the explosive part consists of a few pounds of more or less pure fissile material.

The control of a chain-reaction in which the neutrons are travelling at 15,000 kilometres per second seems at first sight impossible. It is made easier by taking advantage of one of the more peculiar properties of uranium fission. When this occurs, not all of the neutrons released in the process are produced instantaneously. Some are delayed by several seconds, and this gives time in which an excess of neutrons can be prevented from arising, by moving parts inside the reactor. The arrangement can be made automatic, so that a chain-reaction can be held at a desired intensity within very narrow limits for long periods.

A chain-reaction cannot arise spontaneously in natural uranium, yet another peculiarity of the element allows a chain-reaction to be produced in it artificially. The chain-reaction does not arise spontaneously because the heavy isotope 238 easily absorbs the fast neutrons released in casual fissions of uranium 235. However, it is found that slow neutrons are much more effective than fast neutrons in causing fission in uranium 235, and when they are slow enough, they produce fissions more quickly than the resultant neutrons are absorbed in uranium 238.

The effects of neutrons on uranium 235 and uranium 238 depend very much on their speed. At some speeds they react more quickly than at others, as if the nuclei resonated when struck by neutrons at these speeds, and were put into a condition of easy reaction. The practical release of atomic energy has depended very much on the utilization of several of these peculiar features of atomic behaviour.

Fermi showed in 1935 that neutrons were slowed down when they impinged on other light particles such as atoms of hydrogen, or beryllium or carbon. It follows from the ordinary laws of mechanics that an elastic particle loses much less of its momentum in impinging on a heavy than on a light particle. A material used for slowing down neutrons is called a *moderator*.

Fermi utilized his discovery of moderators to produce the first artificial nuclear chain-reaction in 1942. He placed pieces of natural uranium in a large mass of carbon, built up out of bricks of graphite. The fast neutrons from fissions in the uranium were slowed down by repeated collisions with the atoms in the carbon, until they had the same energy as the carbon atoms, i.e. the energy of heat-motion due to their temperature. These thermal neutrons caused fissions of the uranium 235 more quickly than they were absorbed by the uranium 236. By careful design of the sizes and dispositions of the pieces of uranium and carbon in the pile, the chances of the neutrons being captured by the uranium 238 atoms can be reduced, and Fermi succeeded in starting a very gentle chain-reaction. A photograph of Fermi's pile is shown in Fig. 5. A diagram of its internal arrangement is shown in Fig. 6. Fig. 7 illustrates diagrammatically the function of the moderator.

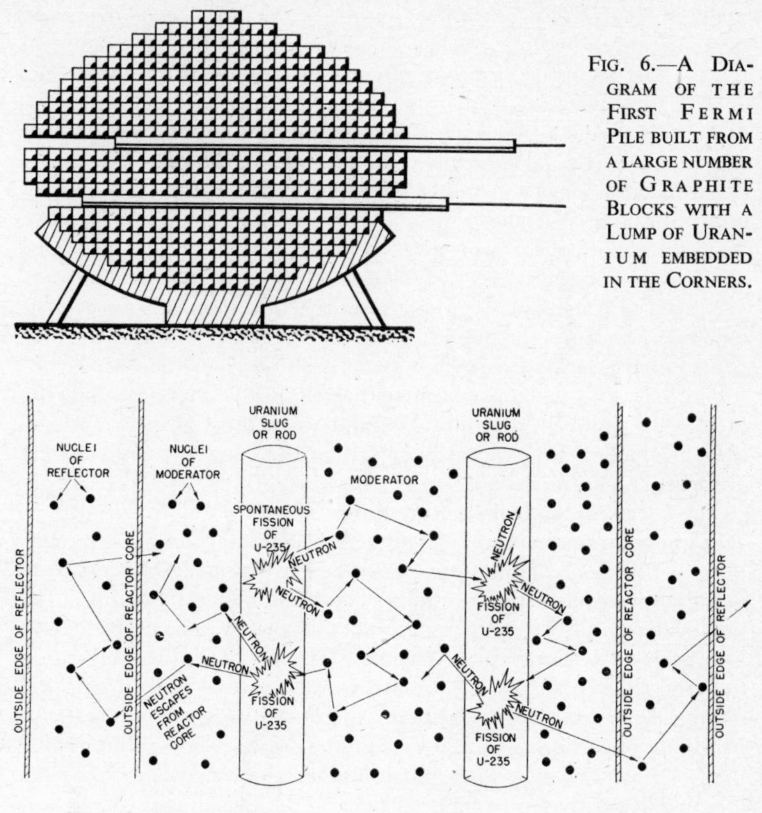

Fig. 6.—A Diagram of the First Fermi Pile built from a large number of Graphite Blocks with a Lump of Uranium embedded in the Corners.

Fig. 7.—The Function of the Moderator in the Fermi Pile.

(*Atomic Energy of Canada Limited*)

Fermi's pile is an example of a slow nuclear reactor. Unlike a fast reactor, it cannot explode. If it got out of control its temperature might rise until its metal parts melted and ran out. The chain-reaction would then die down. Danger might arise not from explosive fragments but from escape of highly radioactive material from inside the pile, and the effects of molten material which might cause an ordinary fire.

The power developed by a reactor depends on the strength of the flux of neutrons streaming inside the volume of its core. Millions of millions of neutrons may cross each centimetre of the core every second, forming a neutron gas or neutron flame within the core in which the fissile material is burnt up, like the coal-dust burnt in the flame inside the furnace of a coal-fired boiler.

Many atoms besides uranium 238 absorb neutrons. Cadmium and boron, for example, absorb neutrons very strongly. Rods of these substances are therefore used to control the production of neutrons in slow reactors. If there are too many, the rod is pushed in, and if too few, it is pulled out. The control is very delicate and can be made automatic.

The first attention was concentrated on uranium 235 because this was the naturally-available easily fissile material. But the properties of uranium 238, which was absorbing so many neutrons in natural uranium, were soon fully investigated. From the point of view of uranium 235, uranium 238 was an unmitigated nuisance, but when it was investigated in its own right it was found to be startlingly helpful.

The neutron entering a uranium 238 nucleus starts a series of transmutations, ending with the production of an atom of the new radioactive element plutonium, as shown in Fig. 8. Even before plutonium had been discovered, it had been forecast that it could

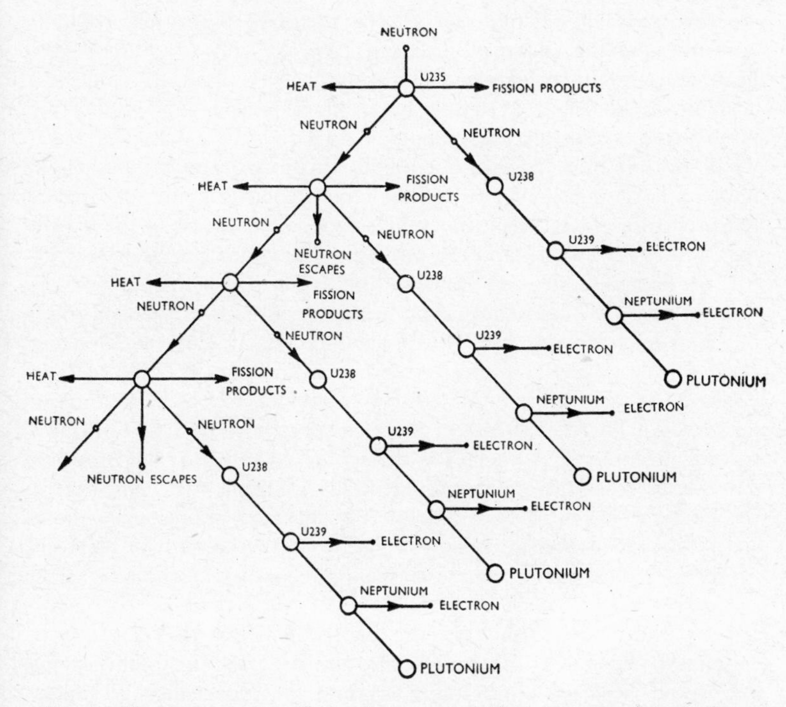

FIG. 8.—THE PROCESS OF A CHAIN-REACTION OF FISSIONS IN AN ATOMIC PILE.

(*Institution of Mechanical Engineers*)

exist, and that it would be easily fissile. This proved to be the case. Plutonium is radioactive and it has a long life which is a very convenient property in a nuclear fuel, though inconvenient in some other ways. A piece of plutonium would take 24,000 years to decay to half its original weight.

The discovery of plutonium provided an alternative source of easily fissile material which did not require the expensive process of isotopic separation by gaseous diffusion, for the plutonium, after it had been formed in the natural uranium by neutrons, could be extracted by chemical methods.

Further, the transmutation of each atom of uranium 238 into an atom of plutonium offered the tremendous prospect of the utilization for the production of nuclear energy, not only of the 0·7 per cent of uranium 235 but also of the 99·3 per cent of uranium 238 in natural uranium. It multiplied the theoretical possibility of the amount of energy which could be obtained from natural uranium by 140 times.

The difficulties of arranging that a reactor should, on balance, produce more fissile material, in the shape of plutonium, than it consumes, in the shape of uranium 235, are great, but they have been overcome in principle. The solution depends on the fact that a neutron absorbed in fissile material produces more than two neutrons. Neglecting those neutron captures by the fissile material which do not cause fission, one might say more graphically that one neutron is required for keeping the chain-reaction going, another is required to replace the uranium 235 nucleus consumed in the fission by a plutonium atom, and the remaining neutrons can then be used for producing additional plutonium. This process is known as " breeding ". The additional plutonium produced at the beginning of the process may be small, but it accumulates at an ever-increasing rate, so that after a number of years the amount of fissile fuel, in addition to the uranium 235 found in nature, will be substantially increased. There is already a practical possibility that, in addition to each uranium 235 nucleus which is utilized, five or six uranium 238 nuclei could also be utilized. This multiplies the amount of prospective energy to be obtained from natural uranium by about six. The raising of the factor towards the ultimate 140 depends on the improvement of the technique and economics of the breeding process.

Even more interesting are the prospects from thorium. It is estimated that there is as much thorium as uranium in the earth, and some experts believe there is three or four times as much. Thorium is in various ways less difficult to work than uranium. It is converted by neutrons, through a series of transmutations, into another isotope of uranium, uranium 233, which is also easily fissile. It seems probable that the breeding process will ultimately be applied successfully to thorium, thus multiplying by several times the amount of fuel in the world from which nuclear energy may be derived by fission processes.

CHAPTER III

VARIOUS KINDS OF REACTOR

THE BRIEF GLANCE we have just taken at some of the fundamental principles underlying nuclear reactors shows that many kinds are possible. A number of the features which may be combined in various ways are given in Table 7, based on one by A. M. Weinberg.

TABLE 7

Source Material	*Nuclear Fuel Obtained from Source*	*Neutron Speeds*	*Moderator*	*Arrangement of Fissionable Material in Space*	*Coolant for removing Heat*
Uranium Thorium	U^{235} Plutonium U^{233}	Slow Fast	Water Heavy water Beryllium Carbon	Heterogeneous, as when rods of nuclear fuel are interspersed with blocks of graphite ; or Homogeneous, as when the chain-reaction takes place in a liquid solution of nuclear fuel	Gas Water Heavy water Liquid metal Oil

The combination of the features in this list totals $2 \times 3 \times 2 \times 4 \times 2 \times 5 = 480$, and the number could be greatly extended by additional possibilities, for example in the form of the nuclear fuel. This might consist of metallic rods, or ceramic made out of the metallic oxide, or a metallic compound dissolved in a liquid, or dispersed or suspended in a foam or mud. When all of the various subdivisions are taken into consideration, about one million different kinds of reactor are conceivable.

This vast range can be swiftly whittled down by consideration of the economy of each of the various factors, leaving about 100 which appear worth looking into. For instance, a reactor contains a quantity of expensive fissile material. It is desirable to extract its energy quickly, so that the minimum of capital invested in the material at any time is resting unused. The problem of the interest on capital investment applies to other expensive materials, such as heavy water, which may be used as a moderator and costs £30,000 a ton. The heavy water required to act as moderator in a reactor might easily cost £1 million.

A water-moderated slow reactor using uranium 233 from thorium might operate at a thermal efficiency of 20 per cent and produce 10,000 kilowatts per kilogram of uranium 233. In comparison, a fast reactor using plutonium and cooled by a liquid metal might operate at a thermal efficiency of 35 per cent, because of the high working temperature, but produce only 1,000 kilowatts of fissile fuel. The output of electrical power by the slow reactor would be at the rate of 2,000 kilowatts per kilogram of nuclear fuel, while the fast reactor would produce only 350 kilowatts per kilogram. This big difference might more than make up for the superiority of the fast reactor in thermal efficiency and in the rate of gain in breeding fissile material.

Heavy water is extremely expensive, but a very good moderator. A uranium 233 compound dissolved in heavy water can sustain a chain-reaction in a solution so dilute that it contains only half a gram of uranium 233 per litre.

In the balance of gas-cooling against liquid-cooling, gas-cooling may give a higher thermal efficiency, but liquid-cooling allows energy to be extracted from the fuel perhaps ten times faster. This is the main reason why the Americans, in their wide range of research on reactor development, have excluded gas-cooled types.

The homogeneous and heterogeneous systems of arranging the reacting material have their respective advantages and disadvantages. The liquid solutions or muds used in homogeneous systems can be given chemical treatment, and heat can be taken out of them, more easily than from the metal bars and solids used in heterogeneous systems. Technique that has been learned in the great liquid-processing petroleum industry can be drawn upon for these purposes.

It is easier to remove the by-products of fission which tend to poison the succeeding fissions from a liquid than from the inside of a metal bar. As experience has shown that the cost of metallurgical treatment tends to be higher than that of chemical treatment, this has been a strong motive for exploring the homogeneous reactor. Its disadvantages are that the reactivity released in it is more difficult to contain, and the corrosion problems that it raises are especially severe.

How long will a nuclear power plant last? Weinberg has remarked that coal power plants become obsolescent through low thermal efficiency. This factor should be much less important in rendering nuclear power plants obsolete. These are more to be compared with hydro-electric plants, and perhaps they should not be more subject to obsolescence than dams. The guide to decision

FIG. 9.—MODEL OF SOVIET EXPERIMENTAL HEAVY WATER REACTOR.
(*United Nations Organization*)

among various types must be sought in the over-all operating costs. In Weinberg's view there are only two certainties, that the slow reactor based on uranium 233 from thorium, and the fast reactor based on plutonium from uranium, will survive because it appears that these systems should utilize the thorium and uranium most completely. But he thinks it impossible to forecast at present which of the numerous types of reactor that can be based on these reactions will prove to be the best, and he thinks it fortunate that the many reactor developments in the various countries are each striking out on independent lines, with little overlapping. This diversity of effort will enable the best types to be discovered more quickly.

Besides numerous types of reactor which are being investigated for research purposes, about a dozen different kinds for producing

FIG. 10.—MODEL OF ARGONNE NATIONAL LABORATORY'S EXPERIMENTAL BOILING WATER REACTOR.

(*U.S. Information Service*)

FIG. 11A.—THE EXPERIMENTAL FACE OF THE *BEPO* PILE.
(United Kingdom Atomic Energy Authority)

FIG. 11B.—A CLOSE-UP OF THE FACE OF THE *BEPO* PILE.
(*United Kingdom Atomic Energy Authority*)

FIG. 11C.—THE *BEPO* PILE CONTROL ROOM.
(*United Kingdom Atomic Energy Authority*)

nuclear power are being constructed or used in several countries. Britain, France, the U.S.S.R. and the United States are working with graphite-moderated slow reactors, cooled by gas, water or liquid sodium. Work is in progress with several types of water-moderated slow reactors using solid nuclear fuel. In some, ordinary water is used, and in others, heavy water (Fig. 9). There are designs in which the water is allowed to boil, and is sent directly through a turbine, or through a heat exchanger to raise steam (Fig. 10). Several kinds of homogeneous slow reactors have been built. Fast reactors are under construction or in use in Britain, the United States and the U.S.S.R. A reactor which has been essential for British development of nuclear energy is the British Experimental Pile at Harwell, generally known as *BEPO*, shown in Figs. 11A, B and C, which are reproduced, together with Fig. 12, from *Harwell—The British Atomic Energy Research Establishment*, by permission of the Controller, H.M. Stationery Office, Crown copyright reserved.

It is a graphite-moderated, air-cooled slow reactor, a longitudinal section of which is shown in Fig. 12. It requires a charge of 28 tons of uranium metal to bring it to the critical stage when the chain-reaction begins. The uranium charge can be raised to 40 tons, which gives an output of nuclear energy equivalent to about 6,000 kilowatts. The energy, in the form of radioactive radiations, is used for experimental researches, such as the collection of data for the design of larger reactors for the production of industrial power, and for the manufacture of isotopes.

The reactor consists of a graphite cube whose edges are 26 feet long. It is built up out of 25,000 graphite blocks, 7¼ inches square and 29 inches long. The blocks are machined to an accuracy of 2½ thousandths of an inch. This was done so exactly that when the blocks were piled up to form the 26-foot cube, its height was correct within three-hundredths of an inch.

Through the cube pass 1,849 channels of about 3½ sq. in. cross-section. Into the central 900 of these channels are inserted uranium bars 12 inches long and 0·9 inch in diameter, which are encased in aluminium to prevent oxidation and the escape of radioactive products formed in the rods. The rods are disposed in the channels in such a way that they are within a cylindrical volume 20 feet in diameter and 20 feet long. This volume lies within the cube, surrounded by a layer of at least 3 feet of graphite, which acts as a reflector that prevents the neutrons arising in the uranium from escaping. In addition to the channels for the uranium bars, there are others for the insertion of materials to be irradiated, and for providing beams of neutrons.

The core of the reactor is surrounded with a lining of cast iron

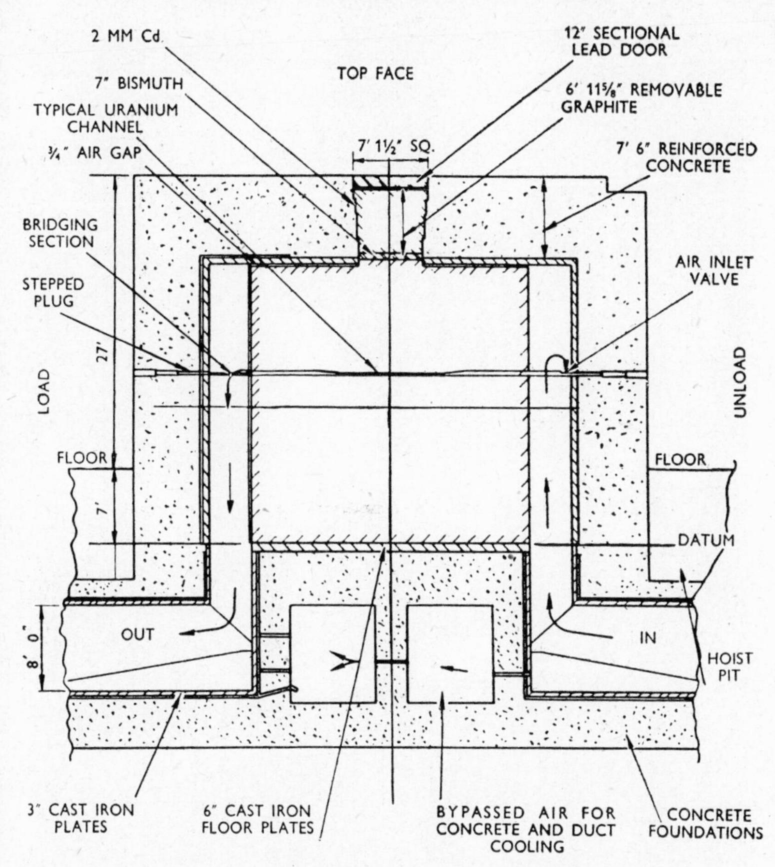

FIG. 12.—LONGITUDINAL SECTION OF *BEPO*.

(*United Kingdom Atomic Energy Authority*)

6 inches thick, backed by thick walls containing 3,000 tons of concrete and 600 tons of steel.

The reactor is cooled by drawing air through it at 180,000 cubic feet per minute. The air is filtered to remove all radioactive matter before it is discharged into a chimney-stack 200 feet high. It is drawn by four compressors developing together 5,600 h.p., driven by 11,000-volt current from the National Grid. In a year, about 36 million tons of air are pumped through this reactor.

The rate of the nuclear reaction is governed by systems of hollow steel rods filled with boron carbide, which absorbs neutrons very strongly. They can be pushed in and out of the reactor, until the desired intensity of reaction is obtained.

FIG. 13.—THE "SWIMMING POOL" REACTOR.
(Union Carbide International Company)

The reactor contains 95 experimental holes into which objects can be placed for irradiation. Some 20 of these are being used for making isotopes. Most of the British output of isotopes has been produced by this reactor. As the commercial value of the British sale of isotopes already amounts to £450,000 a year, this isotope

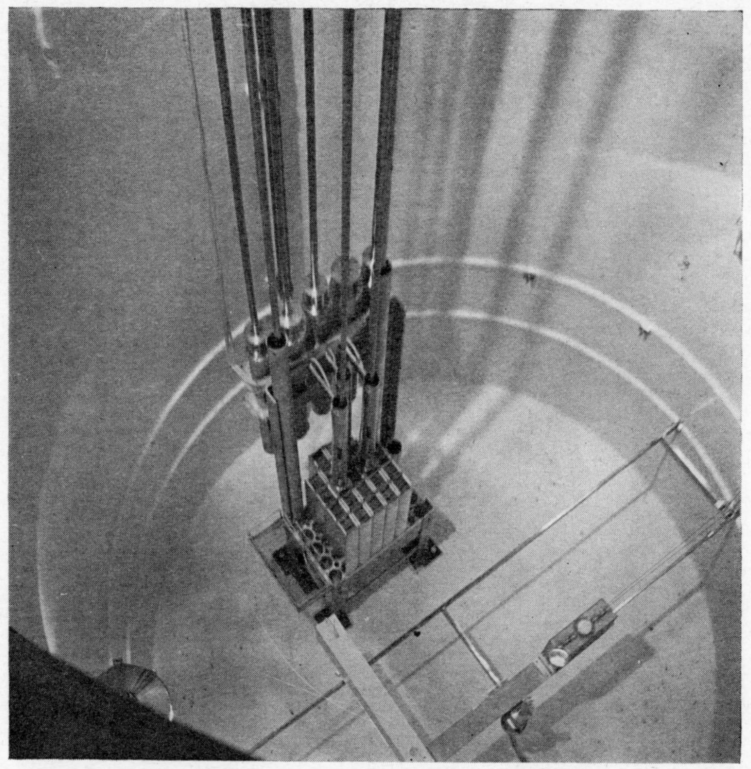

FIG. 14.—INSIDE THE "SWIMMING POOL" REACTOR.

(*United Nations Organization*)

production is already of economic interest. Another 20 holes are used for physical experiments, about 10 for chemical experiments, and half a dozen for the testing of materials under irradiation.

Reactors of this type are simple to use, safe, and adaptable, and provide excellent training for scientists and engineers, besides producing quantities of isotopes, and enabling important scientific experiments to be made.

Very elegant reactors have been constructed, in which water is used as moderator, cooling medium and protective shield. These are known as *pool* reactors. They can be designed so that the reacting core, and experiments made with it, are directly visible. This is an advantage in teaching and training, in research and in the testing of materials. The United States constructed one of these reactors, generally referred to as the *swimming pool reactor*, in the grounds of the Palais des Nations for the Geneva Conference

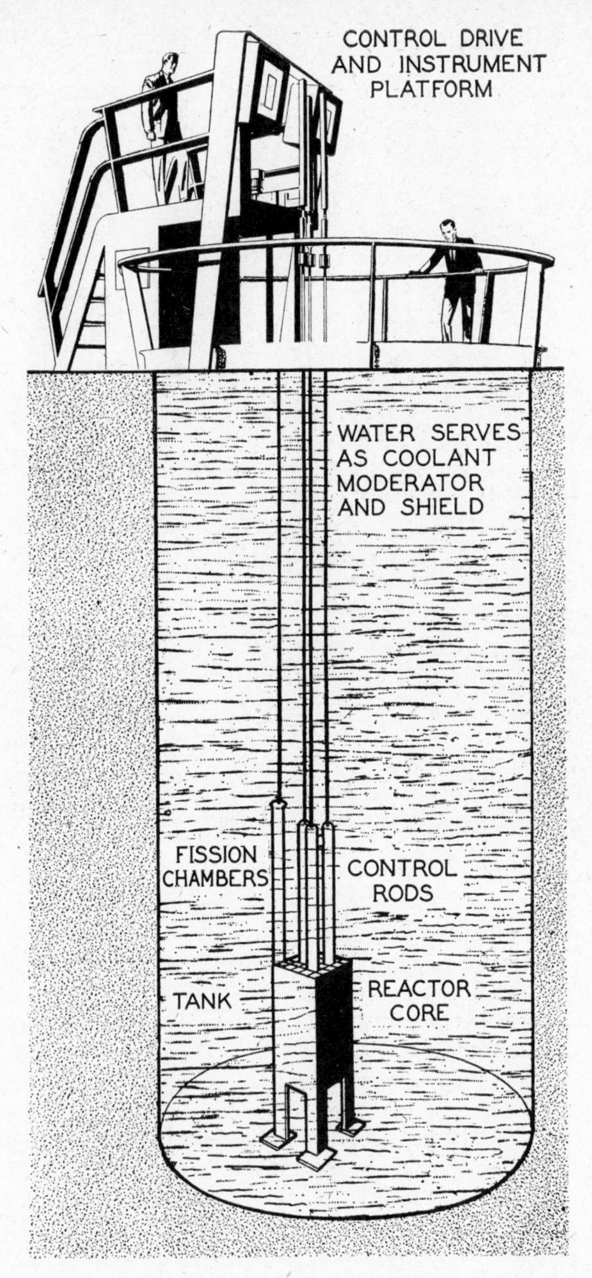

Fig. 15.—Diagram of the "Swimming Pool" Reactor, showing the Control Rods.

(*Union Carbide International Company*)

on the Peaceful Uses of Atomic Energy, two views of which are shown in Figs. 13 and 14. It was open to the public as well as to the participants of the conference.

The reactor consists of a tank of ordinary water, 10 feet in diameter and 22 feet deep. The water is carefully purified by an ion-exchange filter which removes dissolved minerals that might become dangerously radioactive. The fission fuel is uranium, enriched to contain 20 per cent of uranium 235. The fuel is used in the form of uranium oxide which is dispersed in a matrix of about an equal quantity of aluminium powder. The mixture is made in plates 0·025 inch thick, which are encased with pure aluminium sheet. Eighteen of these plates are assembled in a kind of sandwich, with a space of 0·117 inch between, so that water can circulate easily over a large area of the reacting material and keep it cool. There are 23 of these fuel " sandwiches ". They are held in an aluminium grid which is supported from the bottom of the tank. Three of the " sandwiches " have holes through which the control and safety rods can be operated. The total amount of uranium in the reactor is 40 lb., of which 20 per cent, or 8 lb., is uranium 235.

The control rods which govern the reactivity of the core (Fig. 15) are operated electrically, and the mechanism is so arranged that they cannot be removed too quickly. Through this device, the reactor takes about seven minutes to start up.

The depth of water above the core is 16½ feet. When the core is releasing energy at the rate of 10 kilowatts, this depth of water acts as sufficient shielding to reduce the amount of radiation escaping from the surface of the pool to about one-quarter of that from a wrist watch with a radium dial. Radioactive impurities which have been made are continuously removed by circulating the water through a suitable filter. This does not, however, remove the radioactivity arising from the capture of neutrons by some of the oxygen isotopes.

When the pool reactor is working, a beautiful blue glow is produced in the water. It is due to very fast particles shot out from the nuclear reactions. If such particles pass through water with a speed greater than that with which light travels through water, then some of their energy, as they are slowed down, reappears as visible light. The effect was first observed by P. A. Cerenkov in 1934, and explained by Frank and Tamm. By making use of the Cerenkov radiation, the pool reactor can be made to photograph itself. Such a self-portrait is shown in Fig. 16.

The graphic and accessible characteristics of the pool reactor give it great educational value. The student can see what he is

FIG. 16.—SELF-PORTRAIT OF A NUCLEAR REACTOR IN OPERATION, OBTAINED BY USING THE RADIATION EMANATING FROM THE REACTOR CORE AS THE SOLE SOURCE OF ILLUMINATION. THIS IS THE LOW INTENSITY TESTING REACTOR AT OAK RIDGE NATIONAL LABORATORY, TENNESSEE.

(*Union Carbide International Company*)

doing. The reactor can easily be adapted to a wide range of researches, such as heat removal, gas production and stability, which bear on the engineering problems of the development of nuclear power reactors. It is also useful for making small quantities of isotopes.

The Canadian atomic energy organization has built three reactors in its establishment at Chalk River (see Fig. 17). All of them use natural uranium as fuel, and heavy water as moderator. The first of these was built in 1945 in the small wooden building in the left foreground. The second is a powerful reactor, releasing energy

FIG. 17.—THE THREE REACTOR BUILDINGS AT CHALK RIVER, ONTARIO.
(Atomic Energy of Canada Limited)

at the rate of 40,000 kilowatts. It is in the large brick building seen on the right. In the left background a 200,000-kilowatt reactor is being built, and should come into operation in 1956.

The 40,000-kilowatt reactor, known as the National Research

FIG. 18.—THE CANADIAN NATIONAL RESEARCH REACTOR OR NRX, WHICH WENT INTO OPERATION IN 1947.

(Atomic Energy of Canada Limited)

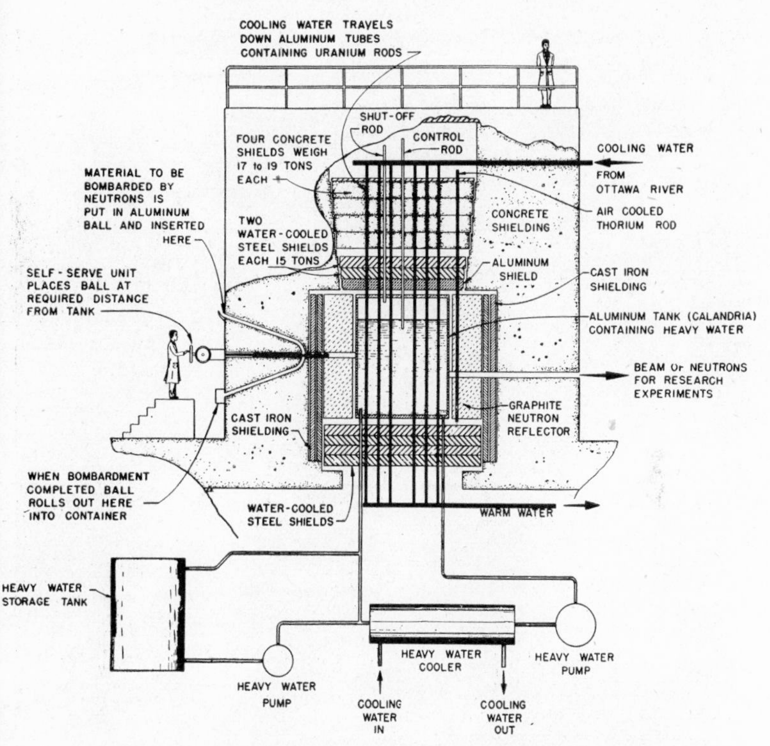

FIG. 19.—SCHEMATIC DIAGRAM OF THE NRX REACTOR.

(Atomic Energy of Canada Limited)

Experimental, or NRX (Fig. 18), went into operation in 1947. Its core has a large and powerful flux of radiation, which has enabled this reactor to be used for many important researches, and for making isotopes which emit exceptionally intense radiations for their weight, such as cobalt 60.

The design of the NRX is shown diagrammatically in Fig. 19, and a model illustrating the parts in Fig. 20.

The outside diameter and height of the structure is 34 feet. The reaction takes place in an aluminium tank, called a *calandria*, which is $8\frac{3}{4}$ feet in diameter and $10\frac{1}{2}$ feet high. It contains 3,300 gallons, or 18 tons of heavy water, which is worth about £720,000. One reason why Canada has specialized in heavy-water reactors is that her large supplies of hydro-electricity enable her to make heavy water more economically than most other countries.

Tubes pass through the tank like fire tubes in a vertical boiler. Their inside diameter is $2\frac{1}{4}$ inches. Within them are thinner rods

FIG. 20.—MODEL OF THE NRX REACTOR.

(*Atomic Energy of Canada Limited*)

of natural uranium sheathed in aluminium. Between the inside of the tube and the outside of the aluminium sheath is a narrow space, or annulus, through which cooling water can be circulated. The rods are 10¼ feet long and weigh 120 lb. There are 176 in the reactor, containing altogether 10½ tons of uranium.

The outside of the tank is surrounded with 58 tons of graphite, which acts as a reflector that directs escaping neutrons back into the tank. The fuel rods are kept cool by circulating water from the Ottawa River through the space around them at the rate of 3,500 gallons per minute. Other parts are kept cool by circulating air at a rate of over 1,000 lb. per minute. The rise in temperature of the cooling water is 40° C. (or 104° F.). The temperature of the heavy water moderator is kept below 49° C. (or 120° F.) by circulating through a heat exchanger at 250 gallons per minute. The temperature of the graphite reflector is not allowed to exceed 149° C. (or 300° F.).

The reactor is coarsely controlled by adjusting the amount of heavy water in the reactor tank and one rod, consisting of a steel tube containing cadmium, is used for the fine control. In addition, there are 18 rods filled with boron carbide, for shutting down the reactor quickly. These are operated by compressed air. The 19 rods slide up and down vacant vertical fuel-rod tubes.

The central space in the reactor, 5½ inches in diameter and 10 feet long, contains an intense concentration of radiation over the whole of its volume, enabling various operations requiring high concentrations of radiation to be performed. It is particularly useful for investigating the properties of fuel elements intended for industrial power reactors.

In the NRX reactor, the production of isotopes has been automatized. Material to be irradiated is placed in an aluminium capsule, which in turn is placed inside an aluminium ball. This rolls down a channel which winds through the shielding around the reactor. A servo-mechanism places it at the proper distance from the tank, and when it is " done ", the mechanism causes it to roll down another winding channel which conducts it into a container. From this the capsule is extracted by an operator shielded from the radiation, and sent to a laboratory for processing.

The National Research Universal, or NRU, reactor to be put into operation in 1956 will have a neutron flux five times as great as the NRX reactor. It will be especially valuable for testing designs of parts for industrial power reactors, making very powerful radioactive isotope sources, and performing research experiments requiring a very high neutron flux. In the NRU the heavy water will be used not only as moderator but also to cool the reacting uranium rods. The heavy water will in turn be cooled with water from the Ottawa River, through a heat exchanger. The arrangement is shown diagrammatically in Fig. 21.

The reaction tank or calandria in the NRU reactor will be 11 feet high and 11½ feet in diameter, containing 43 tons of heavy water. The neutron reflector surrounding the calandria will not,

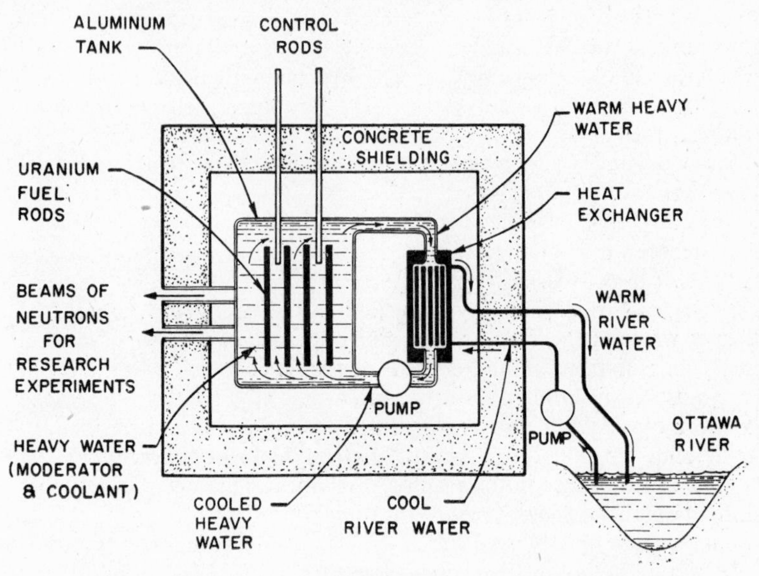

FIG. 21.—THE NRU REACTOR.

(*Atomic Energy of Canada Limited*)

as in the NRX, consist of graphite, but will be a blanket of ordinary water contained in an annular tank surrounding the calandria.

The fuel rods will be cooled by circulating 10 per cent of the heavy water up the inside of the fuel tubes, so that it runs into the moderator heavy water at the top. The heavy water will pass through its cycle at 22,000 gallons per minute and will be cooled in exchangers, transferring its heat to river water passing through at the same rate.

The reactor will be controlled and shut off by 16 cadmium rods. The operation, including start-up and shut-down, will be completely automatic.

The reactor will contain about 200 fuel rods which can be raised out of the reactor into a shielded container built above it. The container, known as a " rod removal flask ", will weigh 225 tons, compared with the 25 tons of the NRX container, and to provide space for it, the building housing the reactor will be 145 feet high.

Figs. 22 and 23 show the NRU reactor in course of construction, and one of the heat exchangers being lowered into position. A model of the NRU is shown in Fig. 24. The figure representing a man standing on the top indicates its size. The reactor is housed in a huge building that has three basements. The main room, which contains most of the reactor structure and experimental area, is about 90 feet high, 175 feet long, and 100 feet wide. The large amount of space above the reactor is necessary to allow the removal of the fuel rods, which are raised up into the 225-ton shielded container or " rod removal flask ". The five vertical tanks visible in the model are heat-exchangers. The various horizontal tubes near the top are holes for introducing material into the reactor. The horizontal layer of transparent plastic one-third of the way from the bottom of Fig. 24 represents the first basement of the reactor

FIG. 22.—LOWERING A COMPONENT INTO THE NRU REACTOR STRUCTURE.

(*Atomic Energy of Canada Limited*)

FIG. 23.—A HEAT EXCHANGER OF THE NRU REACTOR BEING LOWERED INTO PLACE.

(*Atomic Energy of Canada Limited*)

building, and the cellar-level the second basement, containing pumps for circulating the heavy water.

The NRU reactor will cost 49 million dollars.

The Canadian reactors, which are particularly suitable for producing cobalt 60, have helped to supersede dependence on natural radium for intense radioactive sources for use in industry, the treatment of cancer, and scientific research. Canada has already produced more than 29 cobalt-60 beam therapy units, which have

FIG. 24.—MODEL OF THE NRU REACTOR.

The main floor, which comes just above the heat exchangers, and the concrete shielding around the core, have been removed for clarity.

(*Atomic Energy of Canada Limited*)

been installed in hospitals in Canada, the United States, England, Italy, France, Brazil and Switzerland.

Experimental reactors for investigating the methods of " breeding " fissile material (see page 81) are of extreme importance, for

Fig. 25.—Model of the Experimental Breeder Reactor II, designed by the Argonne National Laboratory, uses enriched Uranium as Fuel and a Liquid Metal as a Coolant.

(*U.S. Information Service*)

they provide the key to the most economic utilization of uranium and thorium for the release of nuclear energy. A model of an Experimental Breeder Reactor at the Argonne National Laboratory is illustrated in Fig 25.

CHAPTER IV

NUCLEAR POWER

THE FIRST NUCLEAR POWER PLANT which has regularly generated electricity for industrial purposes was built in the U.S.S.R. and put into commission on June 27th, 1954. The building which houses it is seen in Fig. 26. It has been described by D. I. Blokhintsev and N. A. Nikolayev. The main aim of this pioneer effort was to solve the problem of reliability in the operation of an industrial nuclear power plant, and to provide means for investigating the physics and heat engineering of power reactors. A model of the plant, which was exhibited at the " Atoms for Peace " Conference at Geneva, is shown in Fig. 27.

The nuclear reactor of the power station is of the slow neutron type using uranium fuel and a graphite moderator. The core contains about half a ton of uranium, enriched to a content of 5 per cent of uranium 235, and is capable of generating 30,000 kilowatts of heat. This is removed from the core by water circulating at a pressure of 1,400 lb. per square inch through a primary cooling circuit. This contains a heat exchanger, so that the heat can be transferred to water in a secondary cooling circuit.

It is from the water in the secondary circuit that the steam is drawn for driving a 5,000-kilowatt turbine. Fig. 28 shows a diagram of the cooling circuits.

This system completely separates the turbine and its auxiliary

FIG. 26.—THE ATOMIC POWER PLANT OF THE U.S.S.R. ACADEMY OF SCIENCES IS HOUSED IN THIS BUILDING.

(" *Soviet Union* ")

Fig. 27.—Model of the U.S.S.R. Academy of Sciences Atomic Power Plant, exhibited at the "Atoms for Peace" Conference, Geneva, in 1955.

(United Nations Organization)

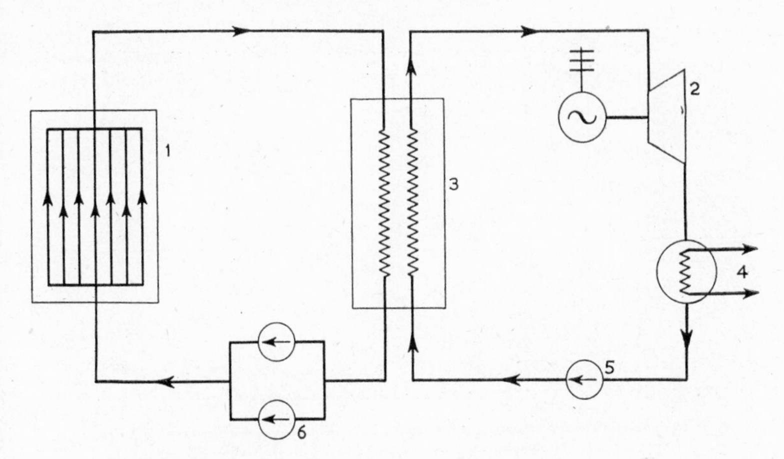

FIG. 28.—DIAGRAM OF THE COOLING CIRCUITS OF THE U.S.S.R. ATOMIC POWER STATION.

1. Reactor.
2. Turbogenerator.
3. Heat Exchanger (steam generator).
4. Condenser.
5. Feed Pump.
6. Circulating pumps.

machinery from all radioactive contamination, so that its servicing is exactly the same as in a conventional coal power plant, and the staff looking after it are not exposed to any radiation hazards.

The use of ordinary water as the cooling medium simplified many engineering problems, but complicated the problem of control, as the chain-reaction in uranium fission is very sensitive to the amount of water in the reactor, which varies with temperature, owing to the change of density, and leakage.

The uranium fuel elements are exposed to an intense neutron flux, and heat is transferred through their surfaces at a high rate. Consequently, the design of reliable fuel elements was one of the most important problems. Proper choice of materials is also a condition of reliability. V. S. Fursov has stated that, owing to war-time conditions, the initial development of nuclear reactors in the U.S.S.R. was carried out independently of other countries. A vast amount of physical and engineering research was done on the relevant problems. It was found that the slowing down of the neutrons through graphite caused it to expand, and its heat conductivity to decrease. The physical explanations of these phenomena were elucidated, and their effects allowed for in the reactor design.

Uranium was found to be even more troublesome than graphite. It exists in three crystalline forms, and changes its size on repeated heating and cooling. Neutrons and fission fragments also altered

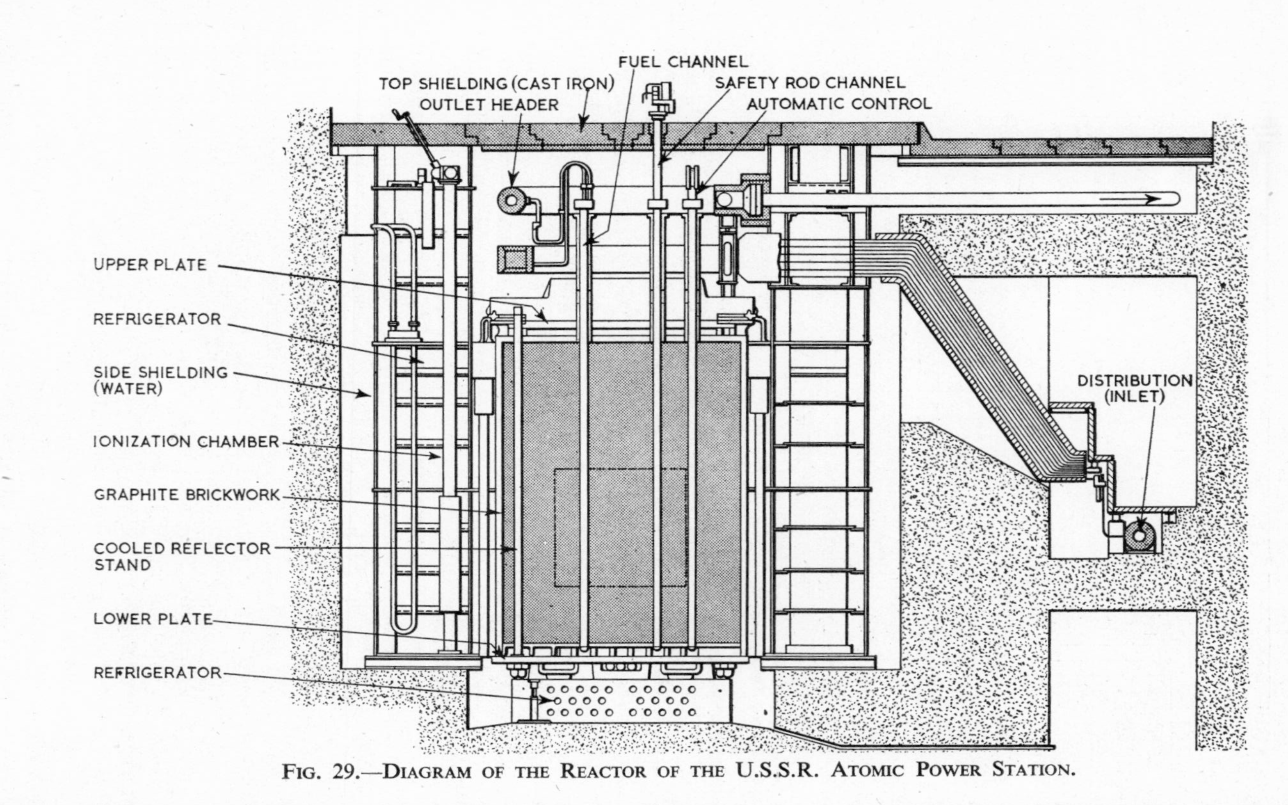

FIG. 29.—DIAGRAM OF THE REACTOR OF THE U.S.S.R. ATOMIC POWER STATION.

its dimensions. It was found that under irradiation its plasticity is increased almost a hundred times.

Stainless steel, on the other hand, became stronger and harder. It contracts, but only moderately. It was therefore a reliable material for the tubes for the high-pressure circulatory system.

The problem of heat transfer from uranium surfaces was studied by the use of models in which the emission of heat was imitated by electric currents.

Finally, experimental fuel elements were exposed in research reactors for thousands of hours, and examined to find which was the most stable and reliable.

The design of the plant is shown diagrammatically in Fig. 29. The reactor is sealed in a cylindrical steel jacket containing the graphite moderator. The interstices are filled with helium or nitrogen to prevent the graphite from burning.

One hundred and twenty-eight fuel channels pass through the core, and contain thin-walled steel pipes for carrying the cooling water, which flows over the surfaces of the uranium elements. These are arranged to form a cylindrical zone in the core, 1·5 metres in diameter and 1·7 metres high.

The-chain-reaction is controlled by 18 rods containing boron carbide, which are moved vertically by wire ropes operated by servo-motors. The flow and temperature of the water, to which the reactor is very sensitive, are recorded on the central control panel for each fuel channel.

A system of regulators keeps the chain-reaction within 3 per cent of the prescribed level. Altogether there are 12 different emergency signals, in particular, for a rise in the chain-reaction of 20 per cent above the prescribed value ; too rapid increase in the chain-reaction ; shut-off of current to circulation current, and changes in flow and temperature of cooling water in the fuel channels. Fig. 30 shows a channel containing uranium being fed into the reactor.

The reactor requires only 60 uranium rods to start the chain-reaction but utilizes 128 in operation. This is to allow for the drop of reactivity when the cooling water becomes hot, and the xenon and other products of fission have also lowered it through their absorbing of neutrons, or " poisoning " effect. Further, it is needed to meet the gradual burning-up of the uranium 235 in the fuel. It was found that with this allowance of fuel, the reactor would work at full power for ten weeks.

Fig. 31 shows the method adopted for storing spare channels.

The reactor heats the water in the primary circuit to about 270° C. This is led to 6 steam generators, each consisting of a water heater, water evaporator and steam-superheater. The primary circuit water leaves the steam generators at 190° C., and is pumped back into circulation. At peak power water is circulated at 300 tons per hour. Fresh water is added to the primary circuit through a group of feed pumps. A hydraulic seal is employed to prevent radioactive water from leaking through the bearings. The radio activity of the outlet water is mainly due to oxygen with a half-life of 7 seconds, while that in the inlet water is mainly due to impurities.

At peak power the plant produces 40 tons of steam per hour, at a pressure of 175 lb. per square inch, at a temperature of 260° C. The steam drives a 5,000-kilowatt turbo-generator.

FIG. 30.—A CHANNEL CONTAINING URANIUM BEING PUT INTO THE REACTOR AT THE U.S.S.R. ACADEMY OF SCIENCES ATOMIC POWER PLANT.

(" *Soviet Union* ")

FIG. 31.—U.S.S.R. ACADEMY OF SCIENCES ATOMIC POWER PLANT.

Spare channels for the Reactor line the walls. Used channels, which are highly radioactive, are lowered into depositories filled with water. The top of the depositories can be seen in the foreground.

("*Soviet Union*")

In the first twelve months of operation the plant produced about 15 million kilowatt-hours of electricity. During this period there was not a single case of a fuel element failing. The automatic control and breakdown protection system worked without a mishap.

The start-up of the reactor from zero to the rated power takes about half an hour, and the steam plant can be started from the cold state in about 2 hours. The fuel elements are replaced every two months, in an operation which takes two or three days.

The reliability of the pumps, generators, high-pressure pipes, etc., was due especially to the great attention paid to the quality of welding. The plant contains several thousand welded joints, all of which were very carefully checked.

Detailed studies of the efficiency of the protection against health hazards from radiation showed that the radiation intensity in the main hall when the reactor was working at peak power was below the recognized tolerance dose. Most of the activity of the gas going up the ventilation chimney-stack was found to be due to argon, made radioactive in the air near the reactor. The intensity of the radioactivity of the gas leaving the chimney is below that which would be dangerous to the population living near the plant.

During the period of operation of the station there has not been a single case of over-irradiation of personnel, and it has been noted that the most important means of preventing over-irradiation of the workers is strict discipline in the observance of operation and safety regulations.

The cost of electricity from the station is considerably above the 10 kopeks per kilowatt-hour of a large coal power station, but comparable with that of a small coal power station of 1,000–5,000 kilowatts.

On the basis of the expenditure with the 5,000-kilowatt plant, a nuclear power station of 100,000 kilowatts useful power is being designed. It will use fuel cheaper than the expensive 5 per cent uranium 235 enriched fuel burned in the 5,000-kilowatt plant.

It is estimated that this larger station will produce electricity at a cost of 10–20 kopeks per kilowatt-hour, a price from about the same to twice as much as the present price of electricity from a large power station using good quality coal. Such a nuclear power station would employ two or three times fewer workers.

Blokhintsev and Nikolayev have given figures showing the saving in material which may be effected. These are shown in Table 8.

They have shown comparative drawings, which indicate that a 100,000-kilowatt nuclear power station is considerably more compact than a coal-fired station of the same power. A nuclear power station and a coal-fired station, each for producing 100,000

TABLE 8

COMPARATIVE DATA FOR 100,000-KW ATOMIC AND COAL POWER STATIONS

Features compared	*Units*	*Coal Power Station*	*Atomic Power Station*
1. Weight of machinery and mechanisms	tons	2,700	700
2. Weight of metal structures	tons	1,250	900
3. Weight of pipelines and armature	tons	300	200
4. Weight of refractory masonry (graphite brick-work for atomic station)	tons	1,500	500
5. Weight of mechanisms of coal storage	tons	2,500	—
6. Weight of rolling stock	tons	300	—
7. Volume of concrete members	m^3	4,000	9,000
8. Volume of buildings (without turbine room and electric equipment)	m^3	75,000	50,000
9. Size of site	hectares	15	5
10. Inner power needs	kW	8,000	5,000

kilowatts, are shown to the same scale in Figs. 32 and 33 respectively.

Figs. 27, 29, 32 and 33, together with Table 8, are reproduced from Conference Paper P/615, entitled " The First Atomic Power Station of the USSR and the Prospects of Atomic Power Development ", by D. I. Blokhintsev and N. A. Nikolayev, read at the International Conference on the Peaceful Uses of Atomic Energy at Geneva, and released to the press on August 9th, 1955.

At the present time it appears that the first large-scale industrial nuclear power plant to come into operation will be in Britain. The chief motive for this rapid large-scale practical development is that Britain's resources in the conventional fuels of coal, oil, gas and water are severely limited, and the need for an additional alternative fuel is more urgent than in vast countries such as the United States and the U.S.S.R., which still have large reserves of conventional fuels.

There is no doubt that the British have tackled the difficult position in which they found themselves, through the consumption of their coal resources and the strain of the Second World War, with ability and courage, and have begun to retrieve their situation with more success than might have been expected. After having founded nuclear science, and then lost the lead in it to others, they might never have recovered. Today, in certain branches of nuclear science, such as the very important field of big machines for accelerating particles which are needed for collecting the data for further

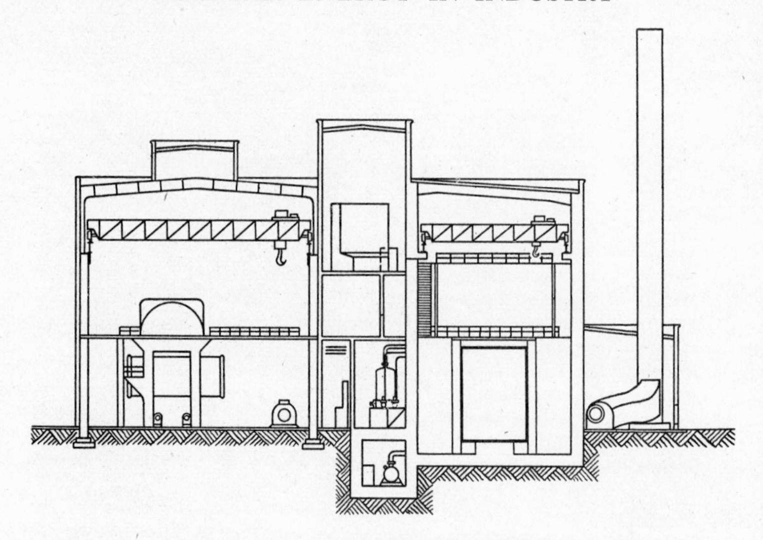

FIG. 32.—CROSS-SECTION OF A 100-MW ATOMIC POWER STATION. (Compare with Fig. 33).

fundamental advance in knowledge of the atomic nucleus, Britain is far behind the United States and the U.S.S.R. It is to be hoped that this situation will be met as boldly as the problem of the production of nuclear power.

The urgent situation in Britain compelled an immediate decision on the kind of reactor that should be chosen for construction on a large industrial scale. As the managing director of the industrial group of the U.K. Atomic Energy Authority, the chief responsibility for taking the decision has lain with Sir Christopher Hinton. It involved the weighing of practical and social considerations, and the compromise between various possibilities, in which the engineer exercises his most important function. In making the decision, the lessons of the history of engineering were not neglected, and Hinton studied the development of the steam engine since the time of James Watt in order to secure guidance on the way in which the new nuclear engineering might develop, and how decisions should be taken today in the light of what happened in the past. The result has been a clear programme, combining conservatism and boldness, which is being carried out with great drive.

When the British development of nuclear energy began in 1946, it was intended to build a graphite-moderated water-cooled slow neutron reactor of the classical type first constructed on an engineering scale at Hanford in the United States. It was to use natural

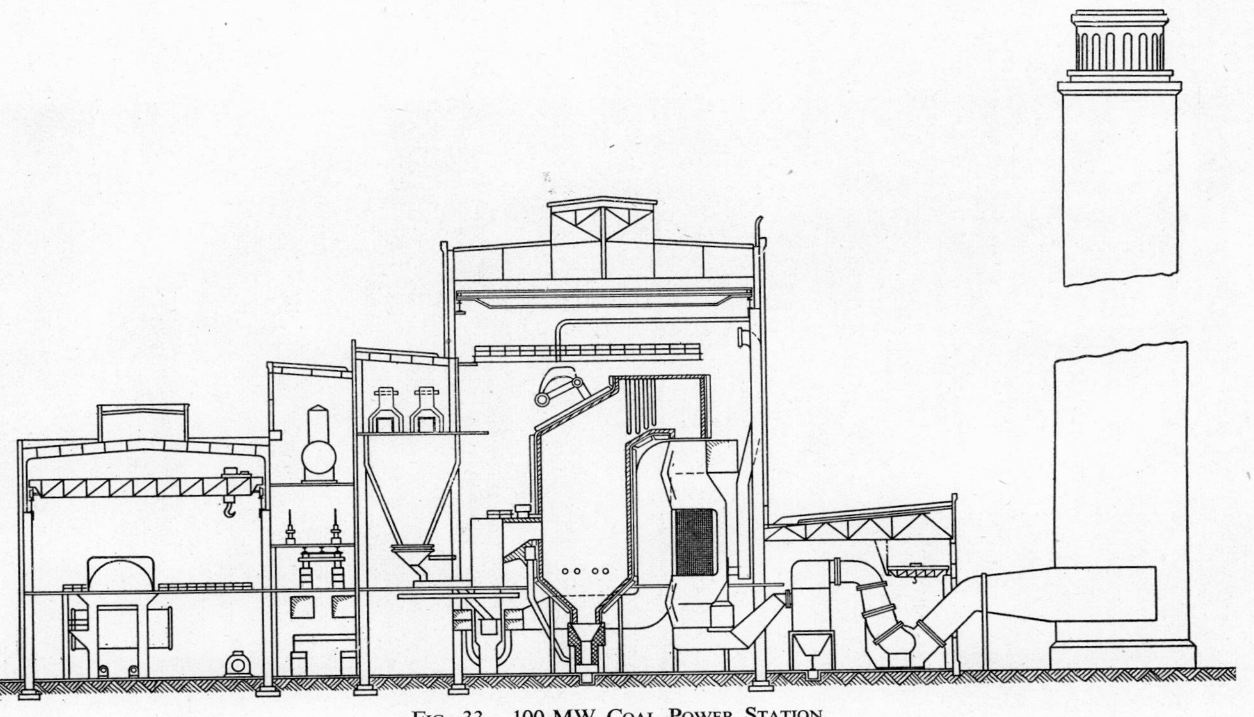

Fig. 33.—100-MW Coal Power Station.
(Compare this with Fig. 32, which is drawn to the same scale).

FIG. 34.—A MODEL OF CALDER HALL ATOMIC POWER STATION.
(United Kingdom Atomic Energy Authority)

uranium, as Britain at that time did not possess a diffusion plant for producing enriched nuclear fuel.

But a water-cooled graphite-moderated reactor using natural uranium is not inherently stable, for if water should by accident leak into the core, it could produce a rapid increase in release of energy which, while it would not produce an explosion, might melt and destroy the reactor, perhaps discharging large quantities of lethal radioactive substances into the atmosphere. This danger was minimized in America by choosing a site in the State of Washington, in the sparsely-inhabited north-west region of the continent.

In Britain, owing to the dense population, no convenient site could be found sufficiently far from the main centres of population to be considered safe for the use of a water-cooled graphite-moderated reactor. It was therefore decided to adopt gas-cooling, for in case of accident, should the gas escape, the reactivity in the core would die down, like the collapse of a tyre after being punctured. In the British situation, the graphite gas-cooled reactor had the great advantages that it would work with natural uranium, it was very safe, and it did not require any exotic materials for its construction.

The first big British reactors were therefore of the gas-cooled type, and were erected at Windscale in Cumberland. They were, however, for the production of plutonium, not for the production of power.

When it was decided in 1953 to construct big reactors (primarily but not entirely) for power, it was decided to place them at Calder Hall, beside the plant at Windscale, because of the safety of the site and the existing technical services.

The Calder Hall site is quite unlike that of a conventional power plant with its railway sidings or coal wharves. The only access to it is over a bridge, and it is not served by a railway track. None is necessary, because no continuous supply of bulky fuel is required.

The plant, a model of which is shown in Fig. 34, consists of two reactors, with one turbo-generating plant placed in between. A general view of this power station in course of construction during the summer of 1955, showing one of the 400-foot chimneys of the Windscale plant in the background, is seen in Fig. 35. It has been announced that Calder Hall will be opened by H.M. the Queen on October 17th, 1956, when it will begin to feed electricity into the National Grid.

The design of the reactor is shown in principle in Fig. 36, which is reproduced from Conference Paper No. P/406, " The Graphite-moderated Gas-cooled Pile and its Place in Power Production " by Sir Christopher Hinton, by permission of the United Kingdom

FIG. 35.—A GENERAL VIEW OF THE CALDER HALL POWER STATION NEARING COMPLETION. One of the 400-ft. chimneys of the Windscale Factory can be seen in the background.

(United Kingdom Atomic Energy Authority)

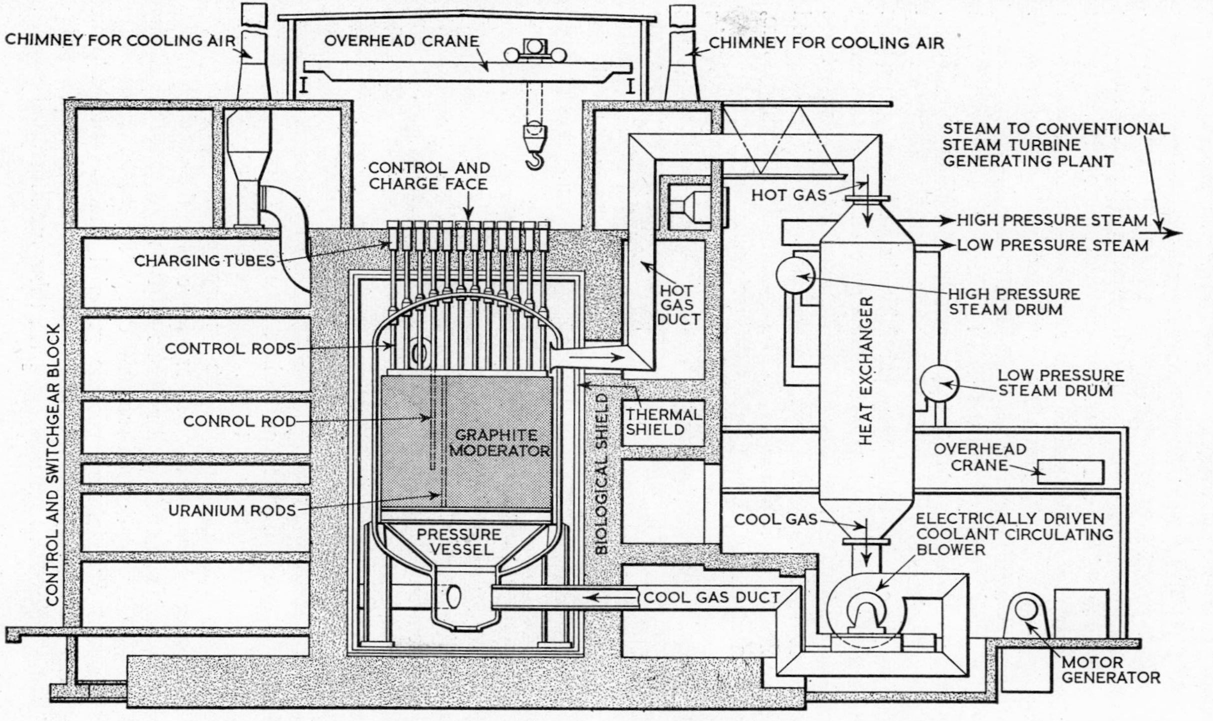

FIG. 36.—DIAGRAM OF A GAS-COOLED REACTOR OF THE CALDER HALL TYPE.

(United Kingdom Atomic Energy Authority)

Atomic Energy Authority. The core is in a large steel pressure vessel, 37 feet in diameter and 71½ feet high. It is made of steel plates 2 inches thick, which were welded into five sections on the site. The vessel, and its outlet pipes, had to be constructed to a standard of accuracy far higher than is customary in conventional engineering of the same magnitude, and two years of preliminary investigation were devoted to the solution of these novel constructional problems. By means of a 150-ton crane 200 feet high, the sections were hoisted to a height of 120 feet, and lowered into the concrete vault which provides the biological shield to protect the staff against radiation. The final welds were made inside the vault, with the assembled sections in place. All welds were carefully checked by radiography. The stresses in the completed vessel were relieved by radiant heating provided by 150,000 kilowatts of electrical current. The vessel was heated to 550° C. and kept at this temperature for 8 hours and then cooled evenly and slowly. It was tested by air at high pressure, and then at a low pressure of 1·4 lb. per square inch.

The graphite moderator piled inside the pressure vessel weighs more than 1,000 tons. In the graphite mass are vertical channels for the uranium fuel rods and the control rods. The latter are made of stainless steel tube lined with boron steel fillers.

The heat is carried away from the pressure vessel by carbon dioxide gas at a pressure of about 100 lb. per square inch. It is pumped through the cooling circuit by 2,000-h.p. blowers. The gas stream is continuously monitored in order to detect burst fuel elements. More than 20 tons of carbon dioxide are needed to fill the reactor and cooling circuits.

The heat in the carbon dioxide gas is extracted in four heat exchangers, each about 18 feet in diameter and 80 feet high. The water-heating surface is 30,000 sq. ft. in area, consisting of the surfaces of 2-inch steel tubes whose area is extended by fixing on them elliptical steel studs. In the eight heat exchangers at Calder Hall there are 250 miles of tubing, bearing 120 millions of the elliptical studs on their outsides. One of the heat exchangers in course of erection is seen in the foreground of Fig. 37.

The tubes for the exchangers were delivered to the site in sections. All these miles of tubes and millions of studs had to be chemically clean, so every particle of rust and dirt which might contaminate the carbon dioxide, and provide material which could become radioactive while passing through the core, was removed by shot-blasting. Stages in the making of the tubes are illustrated in Figs. 38, 39 and 40.

Advantage was taken of the established mass-production technique for making the studded tubes, otherwise such enormous quantities

FIG. 37.—CALDER HALL ATOMIC POWER STATION UNDER CONSTRUCTION. One of the eight 80-ft. high heat exchangers is being erected in the foreground.

(*Babcock & Wilcox Ltd.*)

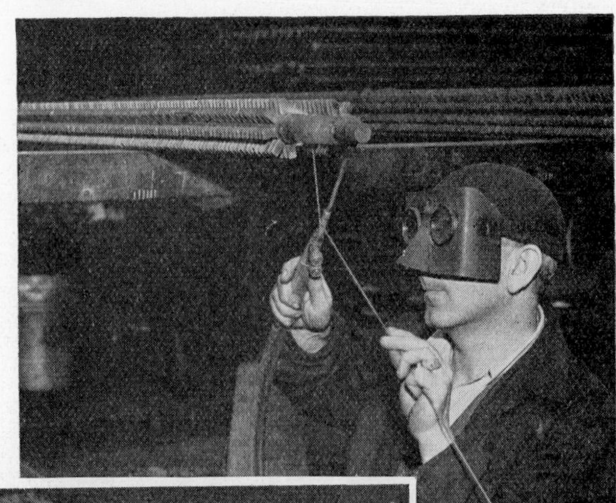

FIG. 38.—SEMI-AUTOMATIC WELDING OF STUDS ON TUBES FOR HEAT-EXCHANGER SECTIONS.

(*Babcock & Wilcox Ltd.*)

FIG. 39.—WELDING RETURN BENDS ON TUBES TO FORM HEAT-EXCHANGER SECTIONS.

(*Babcock & Wilcox Ltd.*)

could not have been quickly made. But they are not ideal for the absorption of heat from the very pure gas. In fact, the problem of taking the heat out of a very clean and pure gas has not yet been sufficiently investigated on a large engineering scale. Conventional plant uses steam and flue gases which, from the nuclear engineer's point of view, are not clean and pure, and its performance depends to some extent on what he regards as impurities in the steam and gas. It appears that big improvements are possible in the design of heat exchangers for working with very pure and clean gases.

The parts of the heat exchangers were welded together into nine sections by Babcock & Wilcox Ltd. at their works in Scotland (see Figs. 41 and 42), and then brought by road to Calder Hall. The lower dome of each exchanger weighs 80 tons, and the exchanger as a whole weighs 200 tons. The welding of each outlet-duct to the plates required a continuous welding run of 26½ hours, carried out by a group of welders working in shifts, three at a time. The sections were welded together in a horizontal position on the site (Figs. 43 and 44), then raised by a big crane into the vertical position (Fig. 45), and set down in their place beside the reactor.

The generator house contains four turbo-generators of established design, constructed by C. A. Parsons & Co., Ltd., each having a full load capacity of 23,000 kilowatts.

The civil engineering work, which has been carried out by Taylor Woodrow Ltd., has involved the construction of large reinforced concrete rafts 130 feet by 107 feet, and 11 feet deep, containing 5,600 cubic yards of material, for supporting each of the reactors. On

FIG. 40.—HEAT-EXCHANGER SECTION ABOUT TO UNDERGO VACUUM TEST.
(*Babcock & Wilcox Ltd.*)

Fig. 41.—Fabrication of Sections of the Giant Heat-exchanger Towers for the Calder Hall Atomic Power Station.
(*Babcock & Wilcox Ltd.*)

FIG. 42.—ANOTHER PICTURE SHOWING THE FABRICATION OF SECTIONS OF THE HEAT EXCHANGERS FOR THE CALDER HALL ATOMIC POWER STATION.

(Babcock & Wilcox Ltd.)

these rafts the concrete walls of the biological shield were built. They are octagonal in shape, to allow for the shrinkage of the concrete. They are 7 feet thick, and rise 90 feet from the raft. A slab of concrete 8 feet thick is placed over the top.

The main civil engineering work on the first reactor building was completed in twelve months. In order to save time, there were departures from conventional erection procedures. For instance, instead of building the big steel pressure vessel for the core first, and constructing the concrete biological vault around it, the vault was built first on the site, while the sections of the pressure vessel were being fabricated in the factory. By following this procedure, about twelve months were saved in the construction of the plant.

FIG. 43.—A VIEW OF THE END OF ONE OF THE 80-FT. HEAT EXCHANGERS BEING FABRICATED ON THE SITE.

(United Kingdom Atomic Energy Authority)

But it involved a number of difficult hoisting and laying operations, so an exceptionally large variety of cranes, which could be obtained without much difficulty, were assembled at the site. Fig. 46 shows the construction proceeding by the aid of floodlight after dark.

The inside of the concrete vault contains an air space of 6 inches, and then a lining of steel plate 6 inches thick, consisting of about

FIG. 44.—ONE OF THE 80-FT. HEAT EXCHANGERS, NOW COMPLETELY FABRICATED PRIOR TO ERECTION IN A VERTICAL POSITION.

(*Babcock & Wilcox Ltd.*

500 of these plates, each weighing about 3 tons. The steel shield is to protect the concrete from damage by heat and radiation from the reactor core.

It is stated that the cost of the electricity produced by the Calder Hall plant will be about 0·6*d.* per unit. This is based on an assumed price for the plutonium which is produced as a by-product in the reactor core. At present, there is a demand for plutonium for military purposes which puts a very high price on it. But the plutonium can be used as a nuclear fuel, both for enriching natural uranium and also in special fast reactors designed for the purpose.

It is estimated that the value of plutonium for these civilian uses is probably £12 per gram, or nearly £5,000 per lb. Even at that price, plutonium is cheaper than its heat-equivalent in fuel oil, as such a large quantity of the latter would be required to produce as much heat as can be obtained from a small quantity of plutonium.

Jukes has given estimates of the costs for a slightly improved version of the Calder Hall plant. These are shown in Table 9. The difference between the figure of 0·76*d.* for the cost of electricity and the 0·6*d.* at which it is expected to be supplied to the National Grid, will be made up from the sale of plutonium.

The actual Calder Hall plant has cost about £16½ million, of which the two reactors together have cost nearly £7 million.

FIG. 45.—ONE OF THE HEAT EXCHANGERS ERECTED ON ITS PEDESTAL AT CALDER HALL ATOMIC POWER STATION.

(*United Kingdom Atomic Energy Authority*)

TABLE 9

COSTS OF GAS-COOLED GRAPHITE-MODERATED NUCLEAR POWER STATIONS (150 MW output)

	Capital Cost £ million	*Annual Cost* £ million	*Cost of Electricity at 80% Load Factor* (Pence per kWh)
Capital and Overhead			
Reactor Items	7·5	0·68	
Other Plant	11·3	0·69	
Total Construction	18·8	1·37	
Cost of initial fuel charge at £20,000/tonne U	5·0	0·20	
Total Capital Cost	23·8	1·57	0·36
Operating			
Site Operating Costs		0·26	
Cost of Replacement Cartridges at £20,000/tonne U		1·46	
Total Operating Cost		1·72	0·40
Total *Gross* Cost		3·33	0·76 (= 9 mills)

According to the Government's programme for nuclear power, 12 nuclear power stations will be built by 1965, and by then will be producing electricity equivalent to the amount which could be obtained from about 6 million tons of coal. The early stations will be of the Calder Hall type, with improved gas-cooled reactors. In these one ton of uranium will produce the heat-equivalent of 10,000 tons of coal. As stocks of plutonium are accumulated from these early reactors, it will be possible to enrich the natural uranium, and burn the enriched fuel in water-moderated reactors. Or the plutonium may be extracted several times over from the uranium, and then utilized again, or re-cycled, in the graphite reactors. This would give heat per ton of nuclear fuel equivalent to 100,000 tons of coal. Finally, research is in progress to develop fast reactors using plutonium, which should enable as much heat to be obtained from one ton of nuclear fuel as from one million tons of coal.

Hinton has compared the gas-cooled graphite-moderated slow reactor with the slow-speed reciprocating engine of the coal and steam era. It is essentially a heavy, land-based reactor, working, as it were, at low temperature and pressure, using cheap fuel and made of familiar materials. It is reliable, and already almost conventional in design.

The fast reactor of the future will be a compact machine, with a very small light core, working, as it were, at high temperature and pressure, using very expensive fuel and constructed of rare and expensive materials. It might be regarded as, so to speak, the gas turbine of the nuclear age.

It is expected that in Britain plutonium will be produced from the early reactors at the rate of several hundred pounds avoirdupois a year by 1964. The liquid-cooled reactors which will probably be using the fuel enriched with plutonium will produce new plutonium more quickly, and provide a rapidly increasing new supply of plutonium for the more advanced reactors of the late 1960's.

The Government has estimated that in the absence of nuclear energy, the Central Electricity Authority would have to invest £1,200 million in coal and oil-fuel stations to meet the increasing demand for electricity. With the development of nuclear power, a substantial part of this sum will, instead, be invested in nuclear power stations. By 1965, in Britain, it may be desirable on economic grounds to discontinue building conventional power plants and turn over to nuclear power for new stations.

The knowledge and experience gained by British industry in constructing these stations will prepare it to enter the export market. While nuclear power stations will immediately be particularly valuable in countries lacking conventional fuel resources and a developed transport system, it is not very probable that such countries could produce much of their own plant, as this would depend on the possession of a highly and widely developed home industry, together with a large scientific and technical personnel.

As part of its advanced programme, the U.K. Atomic Energy Authority is building an experimental fast reactor at Dounreay on the north coast of Scotland. A model of this station is shown in Fig. 47.

The Dounreay fast reactor will be cooled by liquid sodium, or an alloy of sodium and potassium. The reactor and the liquid-metal cooling circuit will be contained entirely in a large steel sphere, 135 feet in diameter (seen on the right of Fig. 47), so that in the event of an accident, radioactive material will not escape from the reactor into the neighbouring atmosphere. The sphere has been designed to resist a maximum interior pressure of 17 lb. per square inch, and a maximum external pressure of 4 lb. per square inch. It is considered that these are the worst conditions to which the sphere might be subjected. The core and control-system have been designed so that an explosion is not possible. Water is to be excluded from the sphere, and the concrete will be covered so that liquid sodium could not come in contact with it. If the liquid sodium escaped into the air inside the sphere it would

FIG. 46 (*left*).—CONSTRUCTION OF CALDER HALL ATOMIC POWER STATION PROCEEDING AFTER DARK BY THE AID OF FLOODLIGHTING.

(*Taylor Woodrow Ltd.*)

FIG. 47 (*right*).—MODEL OF EXPERIMENTAL FAST REACTOR STATION AT DOUNREAY, SCOTLAND.

(*United Kingdom Atomic Energy Authority*)

take fire and the heat produced would raise the pressure of the air. However, the metal surface of the sphere is so large that this heat would rapidly escape through it into the outer atmosphere, which would prevent the pressure inside the sphere from increasing beyond the figure allowed for in the design.

The core is being made in the form of a shielded pot, through which sufficient liquid sodium will be pumped to extract heat equivalent to 60,000 kilowatts. All of the contents of the pot will be removable, to allow for developments in core design.

To secure the reliability of the cooling system, the primary circuit cooling the core will operate in 24 branches, exchanging heat into independent liquid-metal secondary circuits. Each will be operated by an electro-magnetic pump.

The primary circuit will be made of stainless steel to provide strength at high temperature and pressure, and to simplify cleaning. There will be no valves or glands between the free surface of the liquid metal. The pumps will be grouped in pairs, and driven by independent electrical power supplies, in order to avoid the danger of simultaneous breakdown. Each secondary liquid-metal circuit will transfer its heat into a circuit for generating steam for driving turbogenerators.

The reactor core, or pot, will be surrounded by a neutron shield to prevent neutrons from making the liquid metal in the secondary circuits radioactive.

The heat exchangers will be in an enclosure maintained at a temperature which will keep the metal cooling medium liquid. The reactor pot and its neutron shield, together with the heat exchangers, will be inside a concrete bowl 90 feet in diameter and 45 feet high, so that radiations dangerous to health are cut off.

The design of the Dounreay fast reactor is being worked out with the aid of an experimental version, which has been constructed at Harwell. This experimental reactor is on the same scale, but operates at only a very low, or approximately zero energy. It is called *ZEUS*, and is seen in Fig. 48. Its core consists of vertical fuel tubes containing pellets of uranium which has been enriched to contain about 50 per cent of uranium 235. These are mixed with pellets of natural uranium. As the reactor operates at virtually no power, no cooling system is necessary. *ZEUS* is like a full-scale engine which is ticking over very slowly. Nevertheless, by putting an engine through its cycle, even if only very slowly, much can be learned about problems of its operation.

Another experimental reactor which has been built at Harwell to elucidate other scientific aspects of the fast-reactor programme is *ZEPHYR*. This also is a zero energy reactor. Schematic diagrams

FIG. 48.—*ZEUS*, THE EXPERIMENTAL REACTOR AT HARWELL, FOR GUIDING THE DESIGN OF THE FAST REACTOR FOR DOUNREAY.

(United Kingdom Atomic Energy Authority)

of the interior of *ZEPHYR*, and a cross-section of the core and blanket, or envelope are shown, in Figs. 49 and 50, reproduced from Conference Paper No. P/404, " Experimental Studies on Fast-Neutron Reaction at A.E.R.E.", by J. E. R. Holmes, D. D. McVicar, H. Rose, R. D. Smith and L. R. Shepherd, by permission of the United Kingdom Atomic Energy Authority. It consists of a core of plutonium surrounded by a blanket of natural uranium. The core forms a cylinder in space about 6 inches in diameter and length, which contains short vertical rods of plutonium canned in nickel sheaths. The blanket consists of a large cylinder of natural uranium, containing about 8 tons of the metal. As the reactor operates at nearly zero power, no cooling is necessary.

Already very interesting experimental results have been obtained with the *ZEPHYR* reactor. It has been shown that for every plutonium atom which is consumed in the core, two new plutonium atoms are made in the uranium 238 of the blanket. The full-sized fast reactor to be built at Dounreay will use uranium 235 as fissile material. This has not such great breeding potentialities as plutonium. Nevertheless, after allowance for additional absorption of

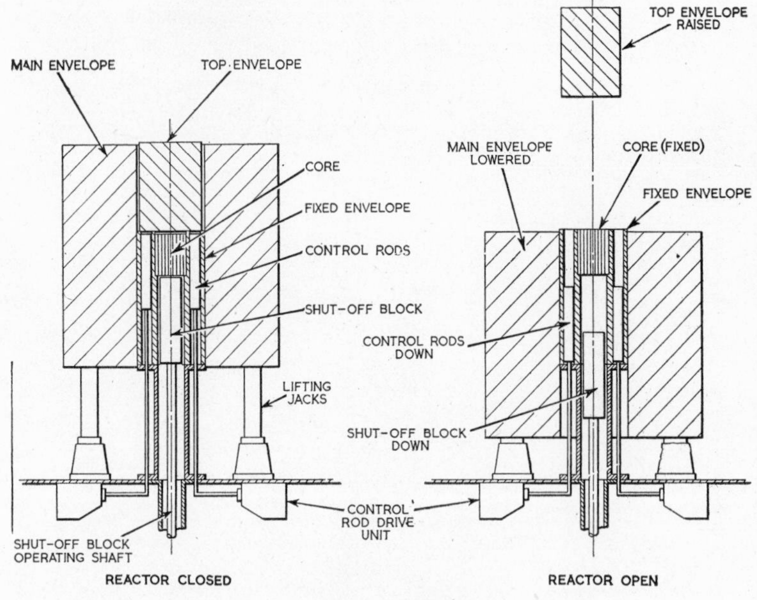

FIG. 49.—SCHEMATIC DIAGRAM OF *ZEPHYR* SHOWING OPERATING AND LOADING POSITIONS.

(*United Kingdom Atomic Energy Authority*)

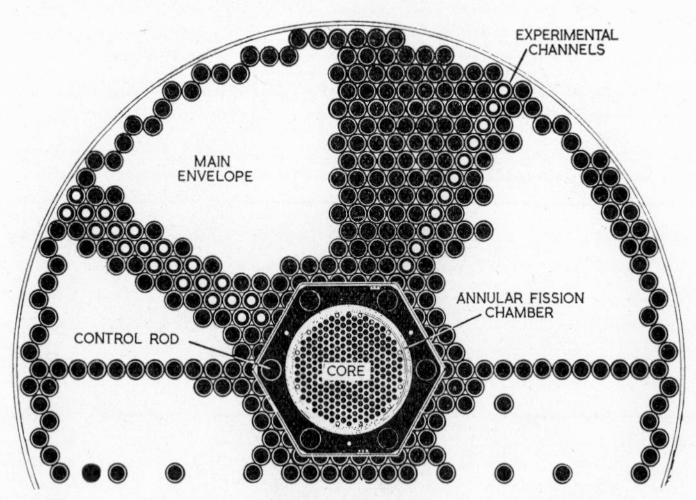

FIG. 50.—HORIZONTAL SECTION THROUGH CORE AND ENVELOPE OF *ZEPHYR* REACTOR.

(*United Kingdom Atomic Energy Authority*)

neutrons by the cooling medium and structural material, a significant gain of nuclear fuel seems assured, perhaps from 50 to 75 per cent. In that case, the original nuclear fuel investment would be doubled by the breeding process in about five years.

The construction of industrial nuclear power plants has not been very swiftly pursued in the United States, owing to the large resources of conventional power, and the strictly economic assessment of performance which is characteristic of the American attitude to technological development. Following from this, the Americans assume that interest at the rate of 12 per cent on the capital investment in nuclear power is necessary, and that amortization of the capital investment should be rapid. Consequently, they conclude that nuclear power in the United States during the next decade will cost from 7 to 10 mills (0·6*d.* to 0·84*d.*) per unit, compared with 5 mills (0·42*d.*) for conventional power (1,000 mills = $1) and will not be economically competitive.

In the military sphere, which is not economically competitive, they have already constructed the submarine *Nautilus*, whose nuclear power plant probably develops 10,000 h.p., at a cost of about ten times the prevailing industrial price of power.

The construction and use of the *Nautilus* power plant has nevertheless provided important experience both in the design and operation of power plants, and especially nuclear power for ship propulsion. Fig. 51 shows the first example of the " Nautilus " type engine, generating power under test.

In the industrial sphere, however, the Americans are not pressing forward with haste. Their plan is to explore the possibilities of many different kinds of reactors, so that the best choice can be made, perhaps in ten years' time, when nuclear power has in their view become quite competitive, and worth a very large capital investment. By putting their major effort into developmental research rather than into the immediate construction of plants, they hope to have the benefit of exceptionally efficient designs in the future, so that their capital can be invested with the maximum profitability.

In consonance with this policy, their present programme of developmental research is broad and deep, and is being pursued with the rich resource and innovation which is characteristic of American technology. They are making big efforts to solve many major problems of engineering design and technological processing such as the use of liquid sodium in engineering practice, and the utilization of zirconium as an engineering material, upon which the production of the high-rated plant of the future, operating at high temperatures and pressures, and using fuel with the maximum economic and thermodynamic efficiency will depend, rather than making low-rated early or primitive types of plant which are immediately practicable.

The U.S. Atomic Energy Commission is accordingly sponsoring five prototype plants of different kinds for the generation of industrial power from nuclear energy. These include a 60,000-kilowatt plant using a reactor moderated and cooled with ordinary water, a 75,000-kilowatt plant using a graphite-moderated reactor, cooled with liquid sodium, a 180,000-kilowatt plant using a reactor cooled and moderated with heavy water, and a 62,000-kilowatt fast reactor breeding nuclear fuel, and cooled with liquid sodium.

Their plants are to be completed by 1960, and the one which apparently will come into operation first is the 60,000-kilowatt plant using a reactor moderated and cooled by natural water. It is to be built at Shippingport, Pennsylvania, about 25 miles from Pittsburgh, and will supply electricity to the lines in that area. Fig. 52 shows an artist's conception of this plant. It will be equipped with a slow neutron reactor, using a combination of highly enriched uranium and natural uranium fuel elements, with a graphite moderator, and a cooling system operating with natural water at high pressure. It is intended to generate at least 60,000 kilowatts of electricity.

The Shippingport power plant is being built by the Westinghouse Electric Corporation, on the basis of their experience in the construction of the power plant of the *Nautilus.*

Natural water which has been very thoroughly purified will be pumped through the core of the reactor at a pressure of 2,000 lb. per square inch. It will enter with a temperature of 508° F., and flow through at a speed of 10–20 feet per second, leaving with a temperature of 452° F. The volume passing through the core will be 45,000 gallons per minute.

After leaving the core, the water at 452° F. will enter heat exchangers, where its heat will be used to convert water circulating in a second circuit into wet steam. The moisture will be removed by a separator, leaving a supply of dry steam at 600 lb. per square inch, which will drive one steam turbine.

Two designs of steam-generator will be used, as shown in Fig. 53, in order to see which proves the better in practice. To guard against the danger of dispersion of the radioactive fission products by an accidental explosion of the high-pressure cooling system, operating at about one ton per square inch, the central parts of the plant will be enclosed in steel containers, so that no dangerous materials could escape.

The reactor container will be 38 feet in diameter, with an 18-foot cylindrical dome. The high-pressure cooling systems will be in

FIG. 51.—THE FIRST ATOMIC SUBMARINE ENGINE, CONTAINED IN A LAND-BASED SUBMARINE HULL.

This power plant, Mark I, is similar to Mark II which drives the U.S.S. *Nautilus*.

(*Westinghouse Electric Corporation*)

cylindrical tanks 50 feet in diameter and 97 feet long, and an auxiliary tank 50 feet in diameter and 147 feet long. The volume of the tanks has been carefully calculated to contain safely the fission products, steam, and other chemical substances which might be suddenly released in the worst conceivable kind of accident.

FIG. 52.—ARTIST'S SKETCH OF ATOMIC POWER PLANT AT SHIPPINGPORT, NEAR PITTSBURG, U.S.A.

(Westinghouse Electric Corporation)

A section of the reactor vessel is shown in Fig. 54. It will be 33 feet high and 9 feet in internal diameter, the walls being 8½ inches thick. The dry weight will be 250 tons.

The reactor core, a cross-section of which is shown in Fig. 55, will form a cylinder in space 6 feet high and 6 feet in diameter. In order to minimize the amount of highly-enriched fuel, this will be placed within a 6-inch layer around a central volume in the shape of a cube with a 2½-foot edge.

The core will contain 52 kilograms of enriched uranium, and the blanket 12 tons of uranium oxide. In the early life of the reactor, about 60 per cent of the power will come from the blanket uranium, and 40 per cent from the enriched uranium. About 8 per cent of the energy liberated will come from the fissioning of uranium 238 atoms by fast neutrons, and a substantial fraction from the fissioning of plutonium, but the major part will come from uranium 235 atoms.

As the interior of a reactor core is radioactive, it is not easily accessible like an ordinary boiler-furnace, and cannot receive the conventional kind of cleaning and repair. Consequently, it should be simple and rugged, and the use of many small parts requiring much machining and small tolerances should be avoided, as a core with such features would probably not have a long life.

The core will be controlled by 24 rods, which may be made of hafnium, or boron steel, or cadmium-silver alloy clad in stainless steel. They will normally move at 20 inches per minute, and be capable of moving at 200 inches per minute under emergency conditions, being attained within one-tenth of a second after an emergency signal.

The enriched fuel will consist of plates of zirconium-uranium alloy clad in another zirconium alloy. Very many materials new

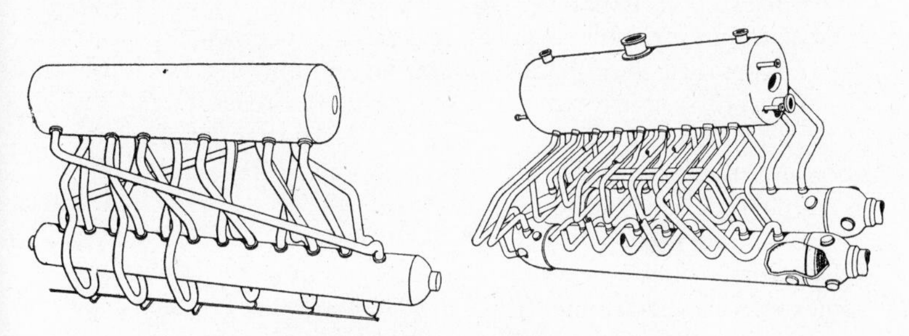

FIG. 53.—TWO DESIGNS OF STEAM GENERATOR.

(a) (*left*) With straight heat exchanger.
(b) (*right*) With U-Tube heat exchanger.

(*U.S. Atomic Energy Commission*)

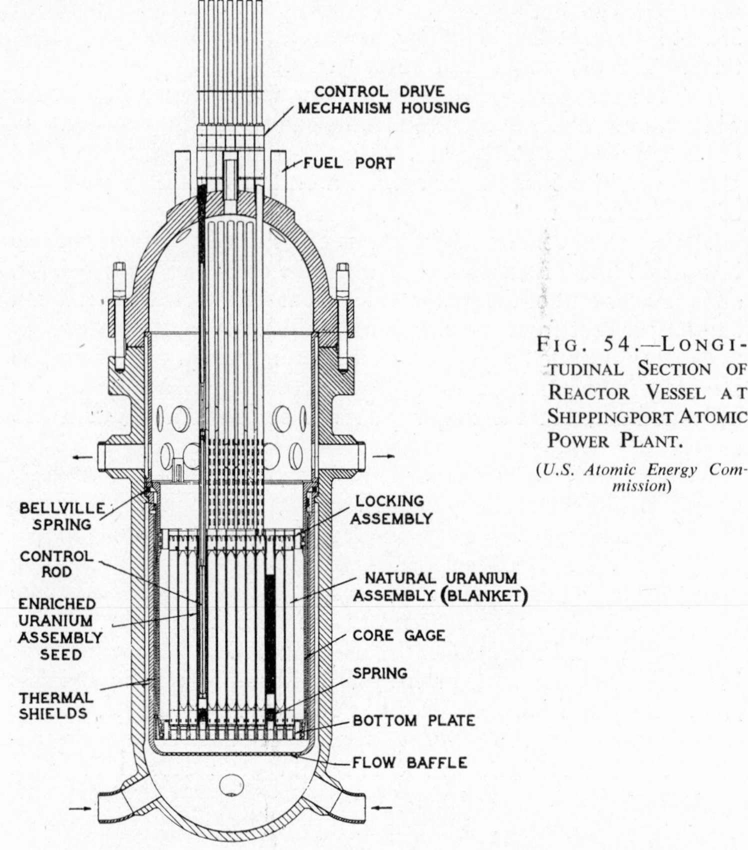

FIG. 54.—LONGITUDINAL SECTION OF REACTOR VESSEL AT SHIPPINGPORT ATOMIC POWER PLANT.

(*U.S. Atomic Energy Commission*)

to engineering are to be used. Even conventional materials do not behave in an ordinary way in reactors. For instance, water at high temperature and pressure causes an amount of corrosion which can interfere seriously with the working of a reactor.

Natural uranium is extremely susceptible to damage from corrosion and radiation. Its resistance can be increased by alloying with molybdenum, silicon or niobium, but these elements catch neutrons.

Uranium oxide is very resistant to corrosion by hot water, and damage from radiation. It is easily compacted into hard pellets which can be very accurately ground to desired dimensions. It is also highly resistant to temperature. At the centre of a fuel rod, the temperature may be 2,000° F., but the melting-point of uranium oxide is about 5,000° F. In the Shippingport reactor it will be packed in tubing made of a zirconium alloy. The processing of this metal is expensive, but its low absorption of neutrons leads to an economy which ultimately compensates for the high first cost.

The engineering design depends on a compromise between many unfamiliar properties. Besides resisting corrosion and radiation, materials should be resistant to wear without lubrication other than that provided by the high-pressure water itself. To discover the best solution, a large number of tests have been made with specimens of various materials, and then with full-size parts.

The Shippingport plant will be designed to operate under a 20 per cent to 100 per cent degree of automatic control. It will be capable of following fluctuations in the public demand for electricity at an average rate of 3,000 kilowatts per minute.

It is estimated that it will have a staff of 130, compared with one of 66 for a conventional station of the same output. 49 of the staff would be for special tests, investigations and security measures, which would not arise in an established system.

Figs. 53, 54 and 55 are reproduced by permission of the U.S. Atomic Energy Commission, from Conference Paper No. P/815, "Description of the Pressurized Water Reactor (PWR) Power

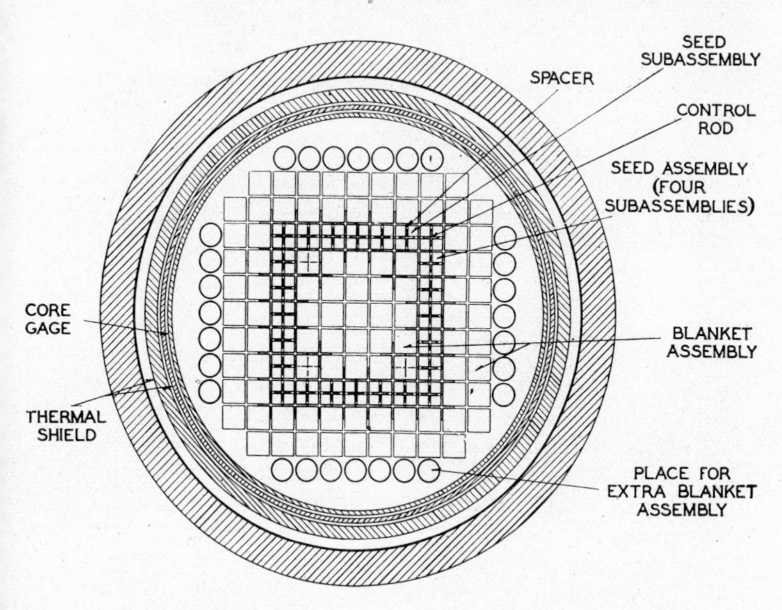

FIG. 55.—CROSS SECTION OF REACTOR VESSEL AND CORE AT SHIPPINGPORT ATOMIC POWER PLANT.

(U.S. Atomic Energy Commission)

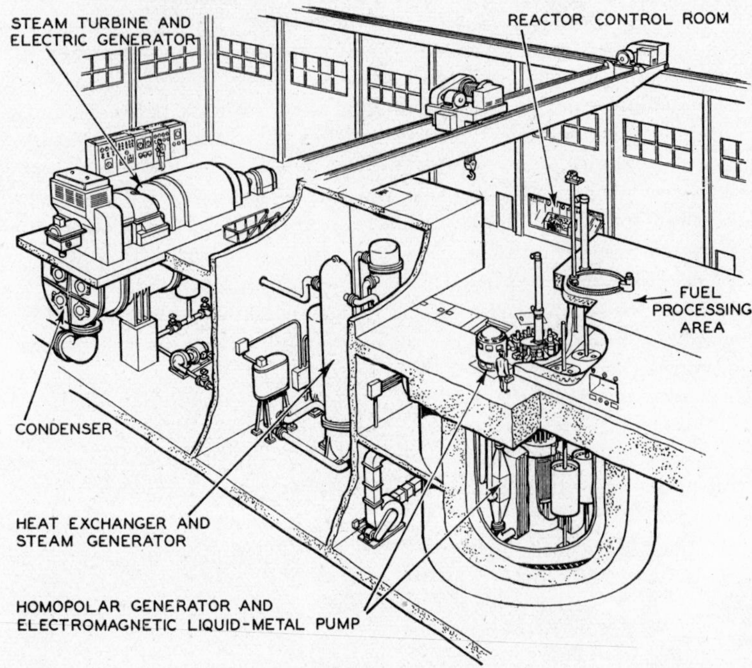

FIG. 56.—A PERSPECTIVE DRAWING OF THE PROTOTYPE POWER PLANT EBR-II, WITH FAST BREEDER REACTOR.

(*U.S. Atomic Energy Commission*)

Plant " at Shippingport, Pa., Part A, " Nuclear Power Generation ", by J. W. Simpson and M. Shaw.

The Argonne National Laboratory is designing a prototype plant with a fast unmoderated reactor, using plutonium as fuel, and cooled by liquid sodium. Construction will begin in 1956, and operation in 1958. It will produce the equivalent of 60,000 kilowatts in heat. A perspective drawing of this plant is shown in Fig. 56.

The Argonne Laboratory has also published preliminary designs for a reactor releasing energy at a rate equivalent to 1,000,000 kilowatts, in which heavy water is boiled as a source of steam for driving turbines generating 250,000 kilowatts of saleable electricity. Fig. 57 shows the section through the central station with this reactor, and Fig. 58 a vertical section through the reactor.

The Argonne Laboratory is building a prototype plant to generate 5,000 kilowatts of electricity in which ordinary water will be used as the moderator, and boiled to produce steam. The perspective design is shown in Fig. 59. A model of the reactor and plant is

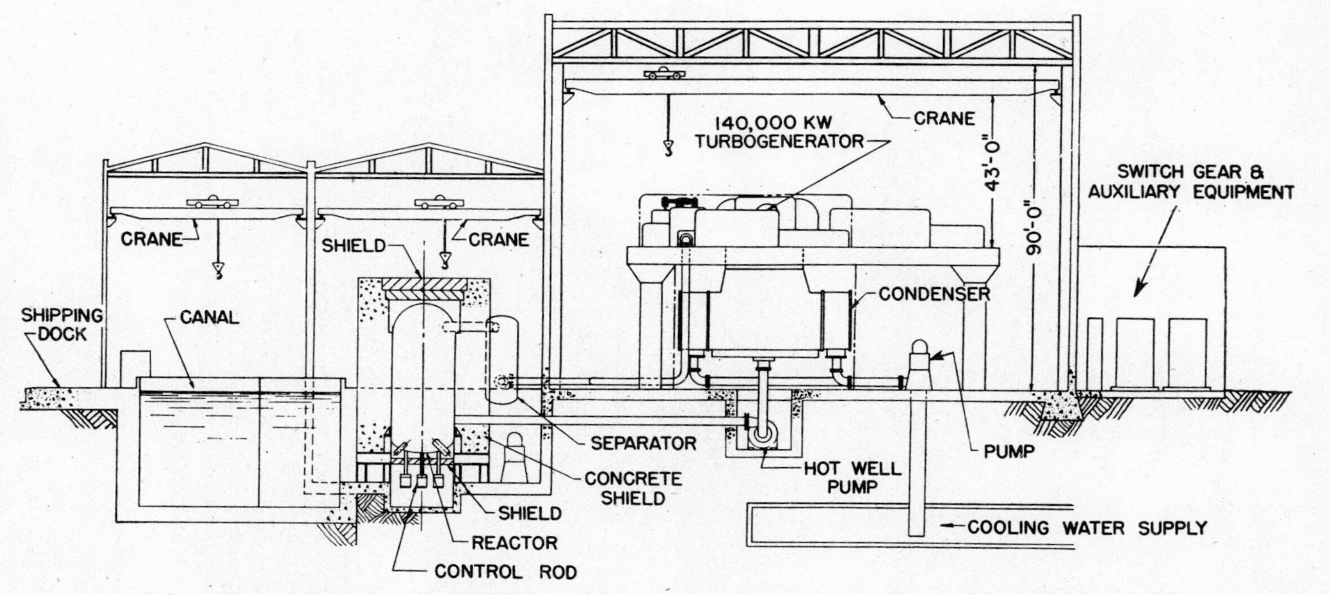

FIG. 57.—SECTION THROUGH THE PROPOSED CENTRAL STATION OF THE 1,000-MW BOILING HEAVY WATER REACTOR PLANT.

(*U.S. Atomic Energy Commission*)

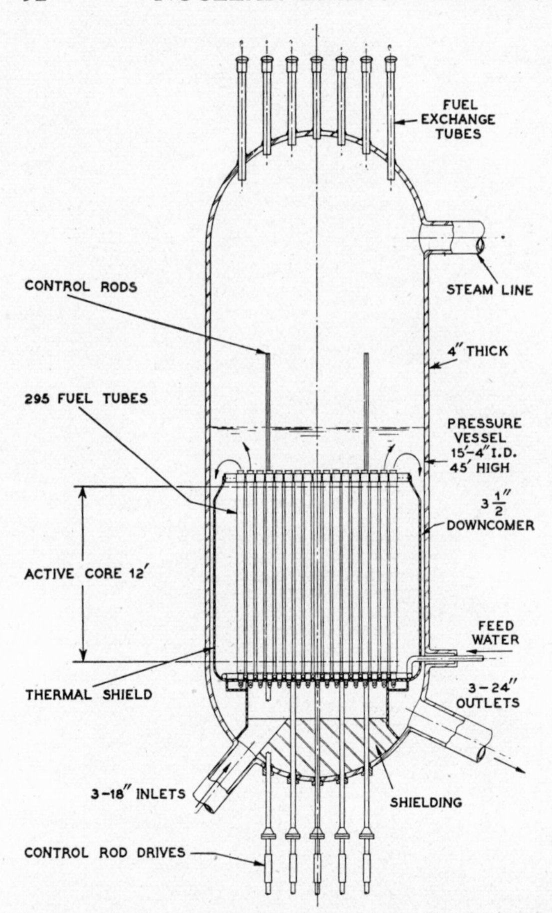

FIG. 58. — VERTICAL SECTION THROUGH THE REACTOR IN WHICH HEAVY WATER IS BOILED.
(*U.S. Atomic Energy Commission*)

shown in Fig. 10, page 33. It is estimated that the construction of the reactor core will cost \$4 million. With natural uranium at \$40 per kilogram, and enriched uranium (85 per cent to 90 per cent uranium 235) at \$15 to \$30 per gram, this prototype should produce electricity at about 33 mills per unit.

The General Electric Company will construct a nuclear power plant generating 180,000 kilowatts of electricity, on a site near Chicago, for the Commonwealth Edison Company and the Nuclear Power Group, Inc. The energy will be released by a boiling-water reactor which, together with the turbine plant, will be housed in a sphere 200 feet in diameter. A model of the plant is shown in Fig. 60.

The Brookhaven Laboratory has elaborated designs for a central

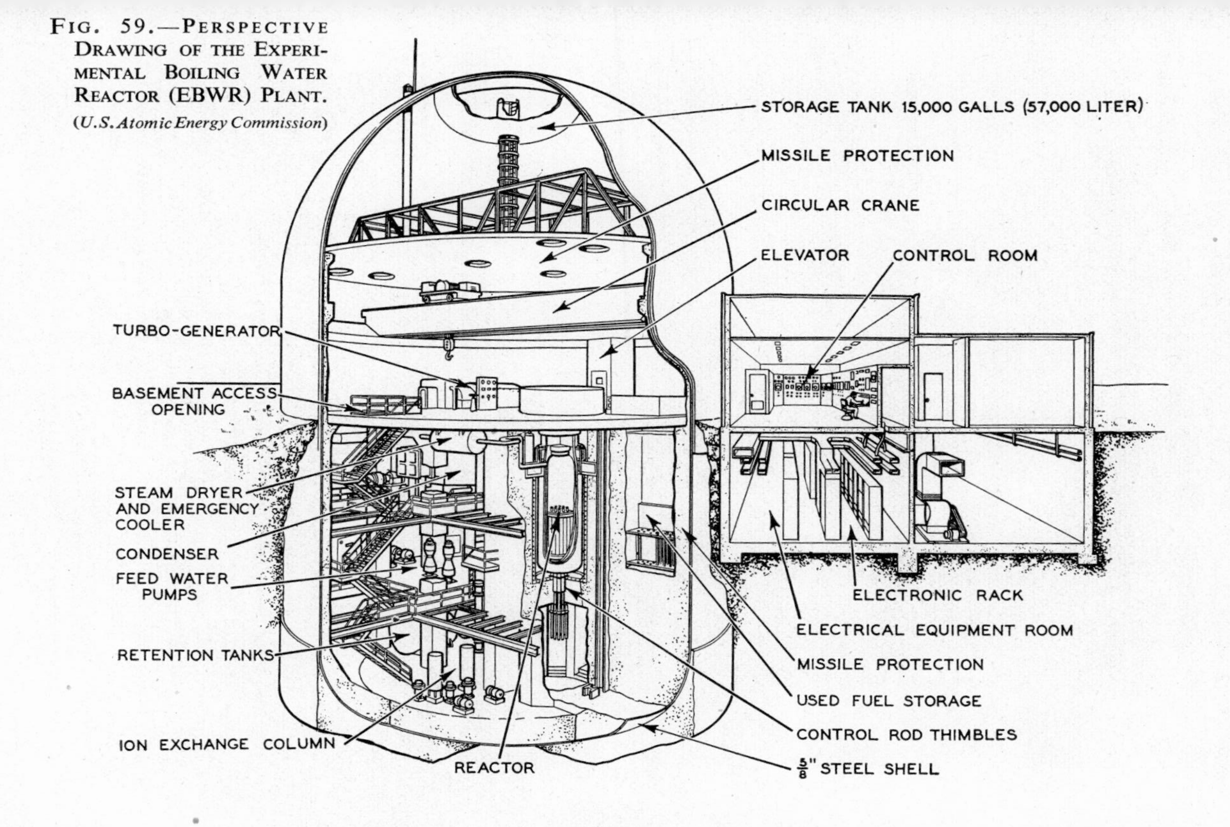

FIG. 59.—PERSPECTIVE DRAWING OF THE EXPERIMENTAL BOILING WATER REACTOR (EBWR) PLANT. (*U.S. Atomic Energy Commission*)

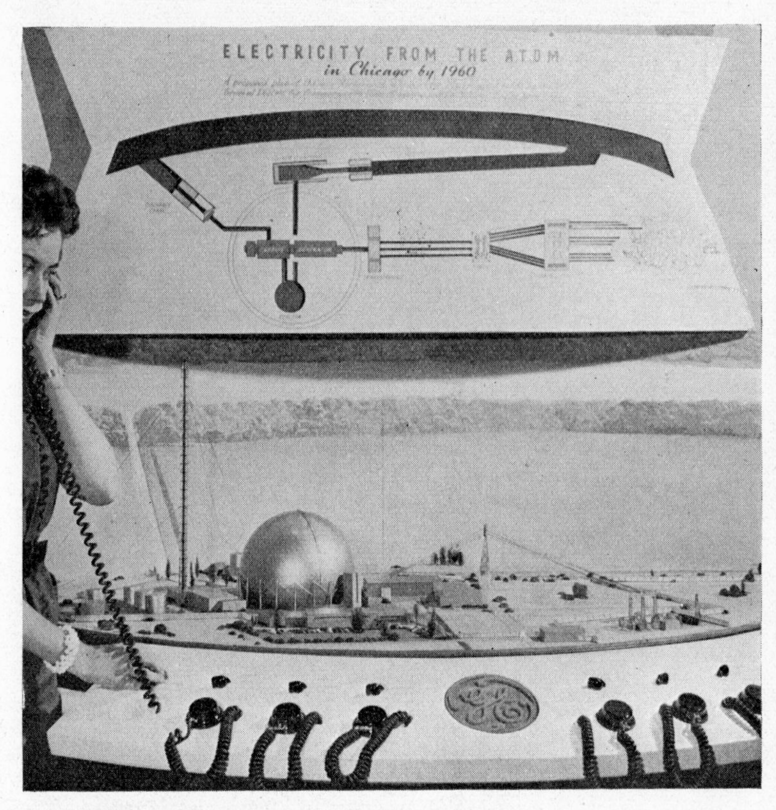

FIG. 60.—MODEL OF POWER PLANT TO BE CONSTRUCTED FOR THE COMMONWEALTH EDISON COMPANY AND THE NUCLEAR POWER GROUP INC.

(*General Electric Company*)

station plant generating 210,000 kilowatts, with a reactor working on fuel consisting of a solution of uranium in liquid bismuth. This system was proposed by Halban and Kowarski in 1941.

The reactor core is surrounded by a blanket of thorium, in which uranium 233 is " bred ", and then used as fuel. Fig. 61 shows an elevation of the proposed plant. The use of nuclear fuel in liquid form greatly facilitates problems of circulation and processing of material. The highly developed technique of the petroleum and chemical engineers in dealing with liquid and flowing materials can be directly utilized.

The Oak Ridge National Laboratory has drafted designs for a central power station in which a dilute solution of uranyl sulphate in heavy water is used as the fuel in the reactor core, and a slurry or

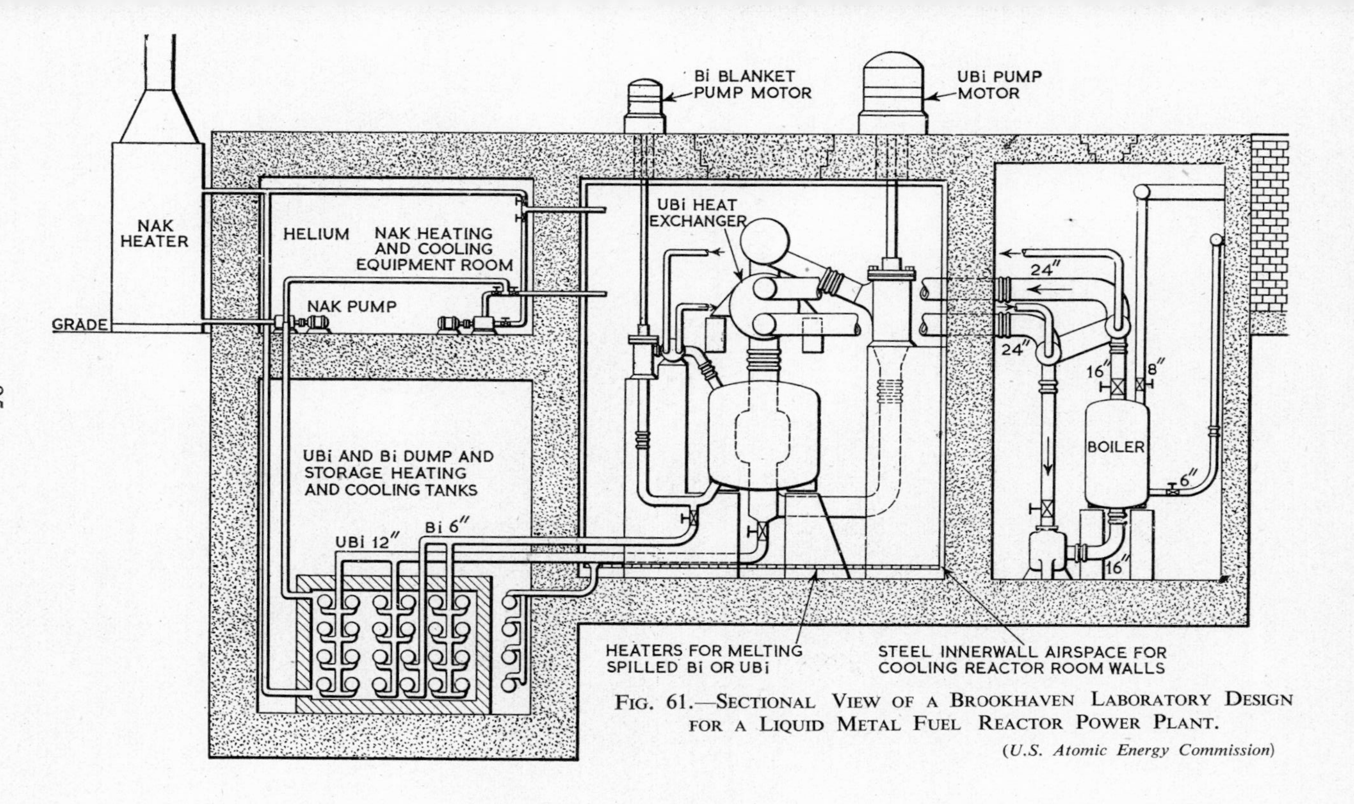

FIG. 61.—SECTIONAL VIEW OF A BROOKHAVEN LABORATORY DESIGN FOR A LIQUID METAL FUEL REACTOR POWER PLANT.

(*U.S. Atomic Energy Commission*)

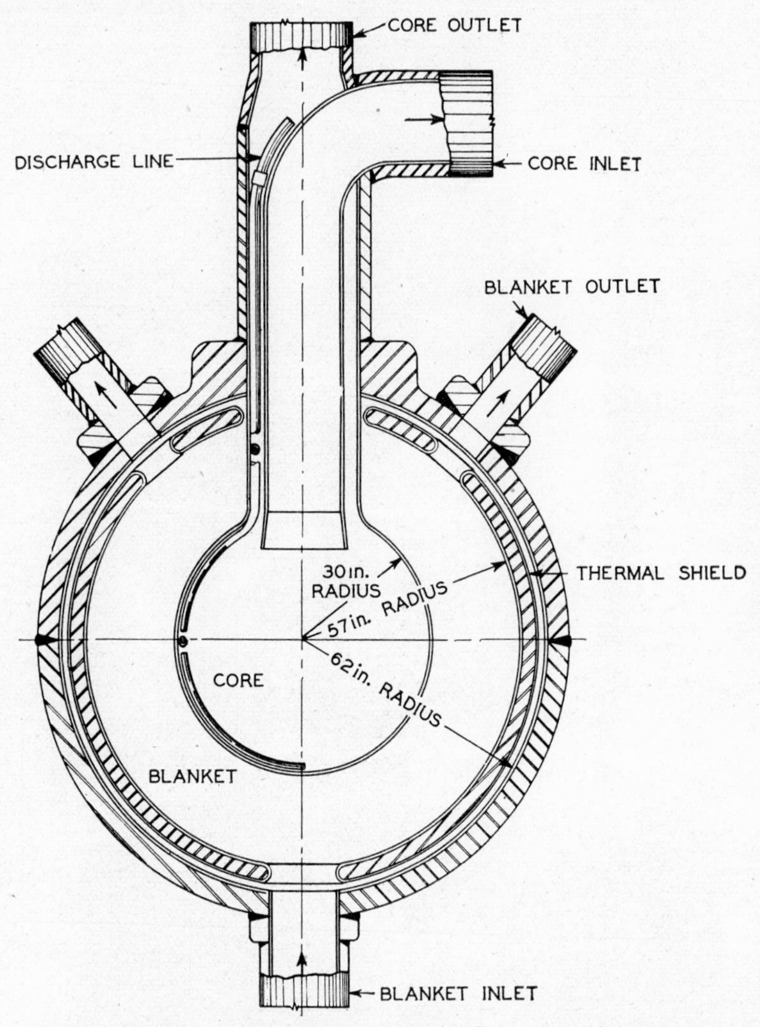

FIG. 62.—TWO-REGION REACTOR WITH "CONCENTRIC INLET AND OUTLET" CORE.

(U.S. Atomic Energy Commission)

liquid mud of thorium oxide in heavy water is used as the nuclear fuel in the blanket around the reactor core. Fig. 62 shows a cross-section of the core and blanket.

In this early stage of reactor technology, like the early stage of the steam-engine, designs are very complicated and various. But in the course of experience and discovery they will gradually be simplified. As Weinberg has said, we do not go to very great trouble to determine the chemical and physical details of the flame in the boiler-furnace of a steam plant, knowledge of its temperature is enough. In the same way, there will be less concern in the future with feeling the pulse of the neutron flame in the nuclear reactor by investigating the detailed behaviour of the neutrons, and the technology of reactors will be dominated more and more by questions of thermodynamics. The homogeneous reactor working with a solution of fissile material in water is already reduced in principle to a pot, a pipe and a pump. The solution comes out of the pot, and is cooled by the pipe acting as a heat exchanger, and then recirculated by the pump. This evolution no doubt foreshadows the conventionalized nuclear reactor of the future, which will be simpler and cheaper than the coal-fired steam-boiler.

The development of nuclear power will be much influenced by the availability of nuclear fuel. The decision of the United States to release 40,000 kilograms (nearly 40 tons) of uranium 235 (valued at $1,000 million) for peaceful purposes is therefore of considerable significance. The United States has also announced that it will release 129 tons of heavy water, 11 tons of which will be available to Britain, and 5 tons to France.

Figs. 56 to 59, 61 and 62 are reproduced, by permission of the U.S. Atomic Energy Commission, from papers read by U.S. scientists at the "Atoms for Peace" Conference, Geneva, 1955. The individual sources are:

Fig. 56 from Paper No. P/501, "The Engineering Design of EBR-II, a Prototype Fast Neutron Reactor Power Plant", by A. H. Barnes, L. J. Koch, H. A. Monson and F. A. Smith.

Figs. 57 and 58 from Paper No. P/495, "Heavy Water Reactors for Industrial Power, Including Boiling Reactors", by H. P. Iskenderian, L. E. Link, M. Treshow and J. M. West.

Fig. 59 from Paper No. P/497, "The Engineering Design of a Prototype Boiling Water Reactor Power Plant", by J. M. Harrer, A. S. Jameson and J. M. West.

Fig. 61 from Paper No. P/494, "Liquid Metal Fuel Reactor", by F. T. Miles and Clarke Williams.

Fig. 62 from Paper No. P/396, "Aqueous Homogeneous Power Reactors", by R. B. Briggs and J. A. Swartout.

CHAPTER V

ISOTOPES IN INDUSTRY

BRITAIN ALREADY SELLS radioisotopes, as an article of trade, to an annual value of £450,000 and the world-production for the market is more than £1 million per annum. The use of a large part of these isotopes in industry has enabled savings to be made in the cost of production of numerous products, leading to a total saving in the world's industry estimated in August 1955 at more than £100 million per annum. Aebersold has estimated that the use of isotopes in American industry saves about $100 million a year, and that in ten years' time it will have increased to ten times that figure.

The rôle of the isotope in industry has been compared with that of the microscope. It is like an instrument or a tool, which has vastly increased the accuracy of many kinds of measurement, and the sensitivity with which minute quantities of substances can be detected. It enables the steps and stages of many technological processes to be followed much further and in far greater detail than any other means. Like the industrial applications of the microscope, those of radioisotopes are endless, and continually developing in new directions. Radioisotopes have novel uses in industry, which arise from their fundamental physical nature.

As atoms with the same electric charge on their nuclei and the same pattern of attendant electrons have the same chemical properties, while the masses of their nuclei may not be the same, it is possible to separate the different atoms, even though they are chemically indistinguishable, by making use of their differences of mass. This is done in the separation of uranium 235 and uranium 238 by gaseous diffusion, in which advantage is taken of the difference in the rate of diffusion of molecules containing uranium 238 from similar molecules containing the lighter uranium 235.

Difference in the masses of nuclei is not the only property by which two isotopes may be distinguished. One of the isotopes may be stable, while the other is radioactive. Some of the atoms found in minerals exist both in the stable and in the radioactive forms. Sixteen of the radio-elements created by nature are still found in the earth.

Molecules containing the radioactive isotope may be distinguished from those containing the stable kind through their radioactivity. Thus the radioactive isotope may be used for tracing the movements and changes of any molecule which contains it. Hevesy began in

1913 to develop this principle into a powerful method of analysis. But at that time, only those few and very special radioisotopes found in nature could be utilized for this purpose.

Then, in 1934, I. and F. Joliot-Curie discovered how to make radioisotopes in the laboratory. The number known was rapidly increased from sixteen to hundreds, and now at least one radioactive isotope of every element is known. The radioactive radiation emitted by isotopes is not all of one kind. There are three sorts of rays, consisting of helium nuclei, electrons, and electromagnetic waves, known as α-, β- and γ-rays. The various isotopes emit one or other of these rays. Further, they emit them with an energy characteristic for the particular isotope. The α-rays do not penetrate air very deeply, but produce a great deal of ionization or electrification. The β-rays penetrate further and produce less electrification. The γ-rays penetrate great thicknesses of dense material, such as steel.

In addition to these various properties, radioactive isotopes disintegrate at very different rates. Some may decay to half their original quantity in a few minutes, others may take thousands of years.

The hundreds of known radioactive isotopes present a remarkable variety of radiations, intensities and lives, and provide a very flexible tool, capable of being used in innumerable ways.

By arranging for the radiation from the isotope to be registered by a suitable instrument, such as a Geiger counter, a photographic plate, or crystals which scintillate when struck by radiations, the whereabouts of the isotope can be discovered, and much can be learned of what the material which contains it is like, and what it is doing.

As radioactivity is not affected by temperature or pressure, it does not matter whether the material is as cold as solid air or as hot as liquid steel; a radioactive isotope in it is quite indifferent to these conditions and its radioactivity always behaves independently of them.

Radioisotopes are consequently able to give information over a very wide range of states, and often when no other means are available. Ever since 1913 they have been of value in scientific research, but they did not become of industrial importance until the development of the nuclear reactor enabled them to be produced in quantity at reasonable prices. In one of the Harwell reactors, about 30 isotopes are produced as by-products of the fission of uranium, and many more can be made by treating substances in the reactor. For instance, if a rod of ordinary cobalt is placed in the reactor, its atoms cobalt 59 are converted by impinging neutrons into atoms of cobalt 60. This is intensely radioactive and emits γ wave-radiations of 1·2 million electron-volts energy, which will penetrate up to 6 inches of steel. The development of nuclear power will bring with it the production of radioisotopes in continually increasing quantities.

Owing to the enormous energy of the radiation emitted, it is possible to detect the disintegration of a single atom. In practice, this enables the presence of extremely small quantities of a radioisotope to be detected. For instance, the phosphorous radioisotope phosphorus 32 can be detected when diluted with ordinary phosphorus to one part in ten thousand million million. The iodine radioisotope iodine 131 can be detected in similar very small amounts.

The phosphorous radioisotope phosphorus 32 has been used by the Goodrich Company for investigating the wear of motor tyres as illustrated in Fig. 63. It was introduced into the molecules of the plasticizing agent, triphenylphosphate, which is used in preparing the rubber. Cars with tyres containing the phosphorus 32 were run over roads, and the amount of rubber worn from the tyres and sticking to the road surface was accurately measured by measuring its radioactivity. With a comparatively small number of runs over the road, it was possible to discover how the wear of the tyre tread was affected by the roughness and composition of the road surface, and by the speed and acceleration of the car, and the way it was driven. Tyres are usually tested for wear by running fleets of cars on them for at least 5,000 miles, which is the minimum distance at which wear becomes measurable by the older methods. The radioisotope method is much less expensive, and much more informative. It has shown, for instance, that the life of a tyre at 60 m.p.h. is only 57 per cent of that at 30 m.p.h.

Radioisotopes have been extensively used for measuring the wear in parts of machines. They enable less than one thousand million millionths of an ounce of abraded metal to be measured. In one type of investigation, the rings on pistons were irradiated in a nuclear reactor, which makes some of the iron in them radioactive. Then the rings were run in a test engine, and a minute quantity of the now radioactive iron which was rubbed off at every stroke, accumulated in the oil-sump. The quantity of iron rubbed off was measured by the amount of its radioactivity. Figs. 64 and 65 illustrate the method used. By these means, it was found that a relatively very large amount of wear occurs in the first few hours of running-in. Examination of the cylinder wall showed that much more rubbed-off iron clung to the surface at the end of the piston stroke than in the middle.

FIG. 63.—TESTING THE WEAR OF MOTOR TYRES.

This is found by measuring the radioactivity of the minute amount of rubber worn from the tyre by towing a counter behind the wheel.

(U.S. Information Service)

Besides giving exact and minute information, the rate of obtaining results is speeded-up. An American research on lubrication, involving both wear and corrosion, obtained results with radioisotopes in four years at a cost of $30,000, which would have taken sixty years by the older methods and would have cost $1 million.

In Soviet investigations on the running-in of aircraft engines, piston rings with narrow channels were given an electrolytic deposit of zinc, containing the radioactive isotope zinc 65. The rate of abrasion was investigated by measuring the amount of radioactivity appearing in the lubricating circuit of the test-engine. An arrangement for doing this is shown in Fig. 66. In this way, the effect on the piston ring of the number of engine-revolutions, of load in the form of revolving moment or torque, of the temperature of the oil and the cylinder-head, of the excess air and type of oil, of the chromium-plating of the inside of the cylinder on the wear of piston-rings, were investigated. It was found that better conditions for running-in could be formulated ; it should be done under a heavier load than had been previously used. The running-in time was reduced by 28 per cent, which lessened the consumption of oil, and greatly increased the wear-resistance of the engine in its subsequent working life.

Fig. 66 is reproduced from Paper No. P/713, " The Use of Radioactive Isotopes in the Study of Machine Parts ", by B. D. Grozin, of the Ukrainian S.S.R., read at the International Conference on the Peaceful Uses of Atomic Energy held at Geneva in 1955.

The radioisotope is used in this kind of research primarily as a physical label which reveals how much, and where the material has been abraded. An important application of a similar kind is in the investigation of very high-speed cutting-tools, such as those made of metallic carbides. In Sweden, cobalt 60, or tantalum 182,

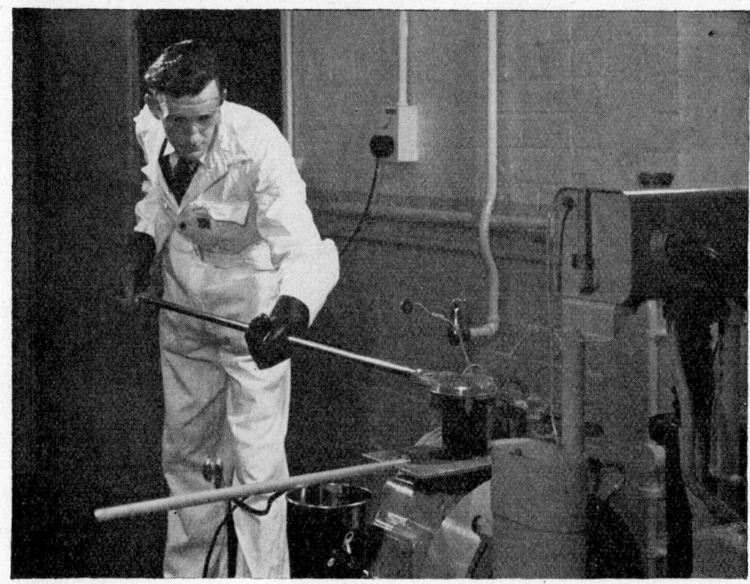

FIG. 64.—THE RADIOACTIVE METHOD OF PISTON-RING WEAR DETERMINATION.
Fitting the Radioactive Top Ring to the Piston.
(*Shell Petroleum Co., Ltd.*)

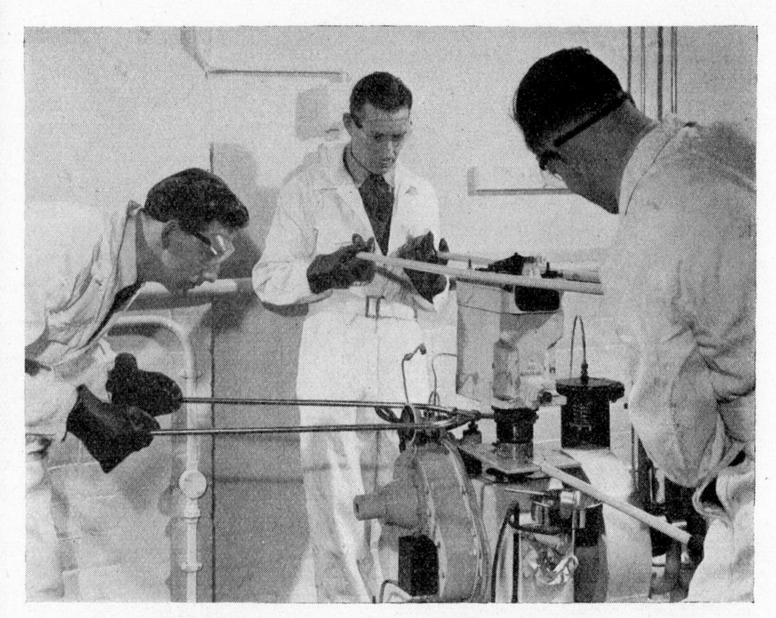

FIG. 65.—TESTING THE PERFORMANCE OF LUBRICATING OIL IN REDUCING PISTON-RING WEAR WITH THE AID OF RADIOACTIVITY.

Here a cylinder block is fitted over a clamp-held piston whose top ring has been rendered radioactive. From the degree of radioactivity in oil samples taken during the run, the amount of wear products deposited in the oil is determined. *(Shell Petroleum Co., Ltd.)*

or tungsten 185 has been incorporated into the carbide cutting edge, and the rate at which the tool is abraded under various modes of operation has been accurately investigated.

In the Soviet Union the determination of the schedules for re-sharpening tools in factories has been based on extensive radio-isotope investigations of total wear. E. P. Nadeyinskaya has shown how the effect of cutting-speed, depth of cut, size of feed and the kind of cooling medium on carbide, high-speed steel and mineral ceramic tools can be measured with the aid of radioisotopes. She has pointed out that the new method by no means eliminates the necessity for the conventional microscopic measurement of the change in shape of the worn tool, for the setting of the tool depends on the geometry of the wear of the tool-cutting surfaces. The combination of the radioisotope method with the conventional method greatly increases the power of solving problems in the investigation of cutting processes, leading especially to the quick solution of practical cutting problems in metal-working factories.

Wear-problems generally concern the abrasion or movement of solids. Another class of applications to which radioisotopes are particularly suited is in the tracing of the movements of fluids. In Britain, which was the first country to be industrialized, and consequently has the oldest pipe-lines, radioisotopes have been much applied to the detection of leaks. Seligman has described how in Glasgow, which has one of the oldest water supply systems, no less than 50 per cent of the water sent to the city is wasted through leaks from the ancient pipes into the surrounding ground. Finding the leaks by the old methods is more costly than wasting half the water-supply, so little was done about it. Now the leaks can be found far more cheaply with radioisotopes.

Three methods have been developed, using the radioisotope sodium 24. A preparation of sodium bicarbonate is made, containing sodium 24 atoms. This is dissolved in water, and some of the solution put into the water flowing through the leaky pipe. After a time, the flow is cut off and the pipe is emptied. The ground around the pipe is then explored with Geiger counters, which reveal where sodium 24 has leaked through the pipe, and stayed in the surrounding ground. This is a laborious method, as it involves much probing with counters. Another consists of measuring the rate of flow of the radioactive solution. If it falls off at some place, this indicates the presence of a leak.

A third method consists of feeding the radioactive solution into the pipe, which makes the ground around the leak radioactive. Then the pipe is washed out to remove the radioactivity from the inside, and the ordinary water-flow is restarted. A vessel which oil-men call a " go-devil " is put into the pipe. This is carried forward by the water-flow. Inside the " go-devil " is a Geiger counter with a recorder. When the " go-devil " passes a place in the pipe where there is a leak, the radiation from the radioactive sodium in the ground outside the pipe discharges the Geiger counter, and is recorded. Outside the pipe, small sources of radioactive cobalt are placed at known points. These also set off the counter in the " go-devil " as it passes by, and are recorded.

When the " go-devil " is recovered from the pipe, the recorder is taken out and played backward. It shows the relative positions of the leaks and the fixed points on the pipe marked by the radioactive cobalt, and so enables the positions of the leaks to be determined exactly.

This method has already been used successfully on pipes up to 20 kilometres in length. It is easy and time-saving, and can be extended to very much longer pipes.

Careful precautions are, of course, taken to prevent any radio-

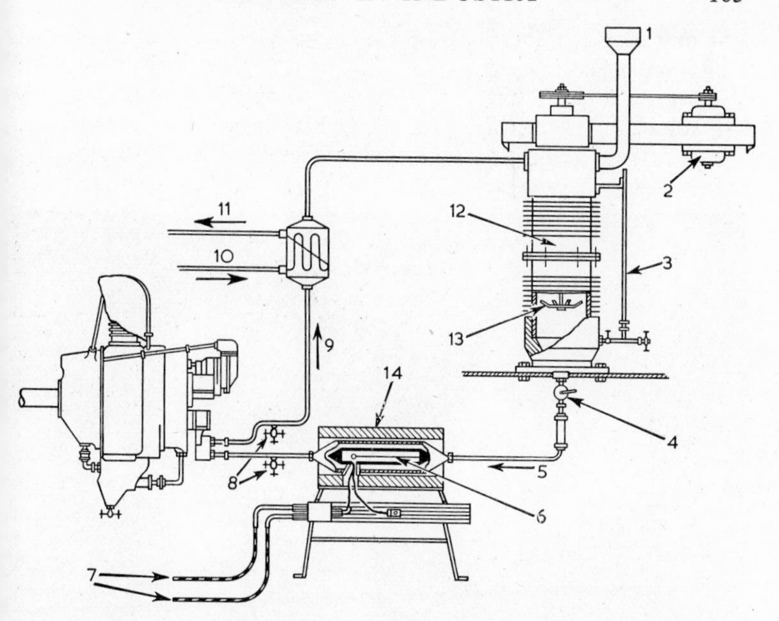

FIG. 66.—AN ARRANGEMENT FOR MEASURING THE AMOUNT OF ABRADED MATERIAL APPEARING IN THE LUBRICATING-OIL CIRCUIT.

1. Pouring in oil.
2. Motor for putting mixer in motion.
3. Measuring tube.
4. Lock tap.
5. In the motor.
6. Counting tube.
7. Wiring to counting apparatus.
8. Discharge tap.
9. From motor.
10. Inlet for cooling water.
11. Water outlet.
12. Oil tank.
13. Mixer.
14. Leak shielding.

activity from getting into the normal water supply system. The isotope used, sodium 24, has a half-life of only 14·9 hours, i.e. it decays to half its strength in that time. Thus it is short-lived, and any traces left after the pipe has been thoroughly washed out with water from the normal supply soon decay to quite harmless proportions.

Radioisotopes have been successfully used in investigations on the possibility of fuel-leaks in aircraft. After the crashes of the "Comet" airliners, the possibility of leakage of kerosene from the fuel-tanks as the cause of the disasters was tested by labelling charges of fuel with the radioisotope palladium 109, in the form of palladium-acetyl-acetonate, or palladium-diethyl-dithio-bromate. A pilot then took up the machine, and performed aerobatics. The structure of the machine was carefully examined to see whether there was any radioactivity on it, and in particular whether there was any near the engines, where leaking kerosene might cause an explosion. The investigation proved that it was very improbable that the " Comet " disasters were due to fuel leakages.

Radioisotopes are used with great effect in petroleum transport. They are injected into the successive batches of oil sent through long-

Fig. 67.—Determining the Type of Oil in a Petroleum Pipfline by means of a Geiger Counter.

(U.S. Information Service)

FIG. 68.—SCINTILLATION COUNTER AND EQUIPMENT FOR RECORDING RADIOACTIVITY IN A BORE-HOLE DOWN TO 6,000 FT.

(*The Radiac Company, Inc.*)

distance cross-country pipelines, to mark the change-over from one batch to the next. If the two batches differ in quality, they may require different handling and treatment, so an immediate warning of the changeover to the operator enables him to take appropriate action before the two batches get mixed. (See Fig. 67.)

The structure of oil-wells is explored by pumping radioactive suspensions into them, and then logging the places where the radioactivity accumulates. In this way leaks, and such important features in the surrounding strata as permeable zones, are revealed. The latter may contain oil, or may be liable to thieve oil from other parts of the well, and their discovery may help secondary recovery of oil from the field, by acting as pathways through which water can be pumped to push out residues of oil remaining in the strata after the primary flow from the well has been completed. A scintillation counter and equipment used in this kind of work is shown in Fig. 68.

Radioisotopes are mixed with the cement which is pumped into wells to block off zones, in order to show exactly where the cement has penetrated. They are added to the water pumped into wells to trace whether it is penetrating into other wells, and they are used in the acid which is pumped into limestone oil-bearing strata to increase their productivity, in order to determine whether the acid is reaching the correct zone.

The same kind of flow-tracing technique is used in following the flow of fluids through the complex systems of pipe-lines in oil-refineries. The flow of catalysts in petroleum cracking plants is monitored by radioisotopes. The use of this technique saved a shut-down in one large cracking plant which would have cost $100,000. The improvement of the flow of oil from wells through information gained from radioisotopes has led to increases of production worth millions of dollars.

The motions of gases can be followed just as well as those of liquids. The vast accumulations of natural gas, trapped in porous strata by impervious strata above and below, are liable to leaks, which may occur around the metal casing walls of wells sunk into the field, and sealed off at the surface. A serious leak of this kind was located by introducing the radioactive gas argon 41, which emits intense γ-rays, into the reservoir. Search with detectors lowered inside well-casings revealed where the argon 41, and hence the natural gas, was escaping. Argon 41 and xenon 133 are useful in investigating such problems as the effectiveness of ventilation systems. Gaseous radioisotopes have also been used very effectively for discovering leaks in gas-filled electric cables.

The Ford Motor Company has conducted large-scale experiments with the aid of radioisotopes on the movement of iron-ore powder in blast-furnaces. They wished to discover whether very finely-divided iron ore powder obtained from the concentration of low-grade ores could be charged satisfactorily into the furnace, or whether it would be carried by the swirling air-blast right through and out of the furnace, without being smelted. Five pounds of the fine powder was put in a nuclear reactor and made radioactive. This was mixed with 22 tons of the untreated powder, and then with 54 tons of coarser ore. The radioactivity of the pig iron and slag, and the dust carried out in the exhaust from the blast, were measured. It was found that 60 per cent of the fine ore powder remained in the furnace and was converted into pig iron. Though the amount remaining in the furnace was surprisingly high, it was not considered high enough. On the basis of this result, it was decided to investigate how the fine ore powder could be conglomerated into larger particles, so that a still higher percentage would be smelted, and make the use of low-grade ores more economic.

As the high-grade ores become used up, the world becomes more dependent on low-grade ores, and the economic significance of researches of this kind becomes very important.

E. S. Kalinnikov and A. M. Samarin have used the radioisotope calcium 45 for investigating the effects of various kinds of linings of furnaces on the non-metallic particles and inclusions which are liable to be embedded in steel ingots. The calcium 45 was introduced into three kinds of bricks made respectively from chamotte, kaolin and high alumina. These were used to line a furnace in which 20 tons of ball-bearing steel was smelted. The non-metallic inclusions were separated from the steel by dissolving the latter by electrolysis, and their radioactivity was measured.

It was found that chamotte brick is five times less stable against slagging than high-alumina brick, and twice less than kaolin brick. The effect of the lining of the ladle was precisely determined. 4 per cent of the total of the non-metallic inclusions in the steel came from the ladle lining when chamotte brick was used. With kaolin it fell to 2·7 per cent, and with high alumina to 1·5 per cent. It was concluded that high-alumina brick was the best for lining ladles. Soviet engineers have made extensive use of calcium 45, phosphorus 32, sodium 24 and silicon 31, for investigating the transition of impurities from the water into the steam in big high-pressure boilers, working up to 2,590 lb. per square inch; and in heat-transfer problems, for determining the distribution of steam in pipes of various shapes and cross-sections.

The silting of rivers and harbours is a problem of great economic and engineering importance, the investigation of which has hitherto proved to be very difficult. Seligman has described how radioisotopes have recently been utilized for this purpose, in researches carried out for the Port of London Authority on the silting of the river Thames. It would have been expected that the silting was due to matter brought down by the river. Thames dredgers remove more silt than the river carries down stream, or is removed by erosion from the banks. This seemed to indicate that silt was being brought in by the tide from the sea.

In order to test this idea, artificial silt was made out of glass containing scandium oxide. The glass was ground down into particles of the same average size as those in the silt, and was irradiated in a nuclear reactor. This converted the scandium in the glass into a radioisotope emitting intense γ-rays.

The irradiated glass particles were mixed with about 100 lb. of the ordinary silt scooped up from the river bottom, and deposited from a boat at high tide on the bed of the river. Fig. 69 shows the dumping gear used for this purpose.

The movement of the silt was followed by under-water Geiger counters lowered from the boat to the river-bed. It was found that the silt sample was first swept downstream. It might have been expected that it would have stayed there, as the fresh water flowing down would presumably have prevented it from coming back. But two weeks later, considerable radioactivity was found in the silt more than 11 miles upstream. This showed that there is an upstream movement of the silt along the river-bed. In fact, five times as much silt is brought upstream by the tide than is carried downstream by the river. In the light of this information, it appears to be necessary to reorganize the system of dredging the river.

The radioisotope chromium 51 has been used in researches of a similar character for tracing the movement of beaches under the tide.

S. E. Eaton has described how several radioisotopes have been used simultaneously in an investigation of the industrial process of continuous glass-making. Radioactive sodium, phosphorus and barium are added to small portions of the various raw materials fed into the machine. By examining the radioactivity of the glass at various stages, the degree of mixing of the materials, and the amount of time that the glass spends in the machine can be determined.

As the radiation from radio-phosphorus consists of electrons, and that from radio-barium consists of the entirely different γ-rays, it is possible to measure the amount of radioactivity from the one isotope in the presence of the other. Preliminary results showed that there was a considerable amount of non-uniform mixing of the glass, leading to suggestions for an improved design of glass-melting tank.

Osipov, Shvartsman, Iudin and Sazonov have used radio-cobalt 60 for investigating the phenomena of mass transfer in the molten metal in a 350-ton open-hearth furnace. They found that the radio-cobalt takes 8 to 15 minutes to become uniformly distributed in the liquid metal when introduced through the middle charging window, and 40–45 minutes when introduced through one of the extreme windows. The experiments showed that the mechanisms of mass and heat transfer in the molten metal during intensive " boiling " of the bath are identical. Convective currents in the molten metal were found to have a speed of one inch per second.

Radioisotopes have been used for the investigation of mixing in many industrial processes, such as the making of paint, ink and plastics. The quality of the mixing can be tested by placing a sample of the product containing a radioisotope on a photographic

FIG. 69.—USING ISOTOPES FOR INVESTIGATING THE SILTING OF THE THAMES. The Dumping Gear.

(United Kingdom Atomic Energy Authority)

film. The radiations will cause the sample to produce an autoradiograph. If the mix is non-uniform, lighter areas will show where the radioisotope is concentrated.

So far, we have been concerned with applications of radioisotopes for tracing the movements of solids, liquids and gases in the mass. The method is equally powerful in tracing the movements of individual atoms. These go through innumerable chemical reactions, and the radioisotopes throw much light on how the atoms thread their way through these reactions, and what places they occupy in the molecules into which they are combined.

Radioisotopes have been used to elucidate many chemical reactions of industrial importance. The heating surfaces of water-tube boilers fired by coal or oil are liable to be fouled with deposits of sulphate. If these are not removed, the boilers must be operated at a reduced load and efficiency, or be shut down frequently for cleaning. It was previously believed that the formation of the sulphate was due to sulphur trioxide in the flue gases. Investigations by Fletcher and Gibson with radioactive sulphur 35 have shown that in the presence of iron oxide, which may be on the surface of the pipes, the sulphate is formed from sulphur dioxide and not from sulphur trioxide. Former attempts to prevent the fouling, based on the belief that it was due to the trioxide, were on the wrong tack.

Steel and metallic alloys consist of the solution of one solid in another. Their hardness, strength and other important practical characteristics are related to this property of being solid solutions. But the movement and arrangement of the atoms in these solid solutions, which underlie their practical characteristics, are not easily investigated. Radioisotopes have been used for this purpose by G. V. Kurdumov and others. They have succeeded in measuring the speed of hardening of steel, which could not have been determined in any other way.

The mobility of atoms in a metal may be measured by depositing a radioisotope on the surface of a thin plate one-tenth of a millimetre thick. It diffuses into the metal and the rate of the diffusion of the atoms can be deduced from comparative measurements of the intensities of the radiation on the two sides of the plate.

The mobility of its atoms is one of the main factors that determine how the metal behaves when it is subjected to stress and to high temperatures. Kurdumov has investigated the self-diffusion of iron in austenite. He found that the presence of iron in the solid solution increases the mobility of the iron atoms at temperatures that are of particular interest for practical purposes.

By researches of this kind, the properties of steel and non-ferrous alloys are gradually being explained in terms of the behaviour of their individual atoms, and the making of improved industrial metals becomes more and more a deductive process, by which the appropriate composition, structure and treatment to produce a metal of stipulated industrial properties is worked out from first principles, and becomes less and less an empirical process, in which the desired properties are discovered by trial and error.

The radioisotope carbon 14 has a particularly important range of industrial applications, for there are innumerable processes depending on the chemistry of carbon. For instance, the processes of the vast petroleum industry depend on it, and already light has been thrown on the reactions of petroleum " cracking ", by which the larger molecules in the oil are broken down to form lighter oils. It has been used, too, in the elucidation of the Fischer-Tropsch process, in which oils are synthesized from materials of non-living origin.

In the synthetic ammonia process much trouble is caused by the " poisoning " of the catalyst, used to promote the reaction, by the oxides of carbon. It has been shown with the aid of carbon 14 that the effects of carbon monoxide and dioxide are identical. In both cases the gases combine with hydrogen to produce water, and it is this water which damages the catalyst.

Various carbon compounds can already be bought from suppliers of chemicals, which contain carbon 14 atoms instead of ordinary carbon atoms. Some of these are particularly useful for investigating the chemistry of fats and oils, and the processes of polymerization. Besides carbon 14, there is also a radioisotope of hydrogen, tritium or hydrogen 3. Detection by tritium is extraordinarily sensitive, and it will probably be widely used both in tracing the movements of gases, and in tracing liquids, e.g. sewage, as a constituent of molecules of water.

In addition to these there are the stable isotopes hydrogen H-2, and of oxygen O-18, and nitrogen N-15, which enable the chief constituents of all living substances, and their products, to be investigated with the aid of isotopes. Their presence and quantity can be determined by the mass spectrometer (Fig. 70). Altogether, more than 1,000 chemical reagents containing isotopes of various kinds can already be purchased as ordinary stock.

In the pharmaceutical industry the amount of vitamin B-12 in source materials is estimated by adding a known quantity of the synthetic vitamin, in which one of its atoms has been replaced by a radioisotope. The material is thoroughly mixed, and a small sample taken from it. The ratio of stable to radioactive isotope shows the

FIG. 70.—A SOVIET SPECTROMETER FOR ISOTOPIC ANALYSIS.

(United Nations Organization)

proportions in which they exist in the whole, and from this the amount of vitamin in the source materials is deduced.

An example of the use of radioisotopes in the animal-food manufacturing industry is the determination of the form in which iodine should be added to salt cake for cattle. It is necessary that the iodine should be in a form which the animal can assimilate, when it licks the cake on the ground, but which is not leached out of the cake by rain or damp. With the assistance of iodine 131, the amount of an iodine compound leached out of the cake by rain could be determined by measuring the radioactivity of the rain-water drained from the cake. The degree of assimilation by the cattle was determined by measuring the amount of radioactivity in the animals' bodies by prospecting the outsides of their bodies with detectors. It was concluded that the most suitable compound for putting into the cake is dithymol diiodide.

Radioisotopes are of great assistance in exploring the phenomena of polymerization, on which the synthetic plastics industry depends. They reveal information which cannot be obtained in any other way, on how the constituent molecules in these materials are bonded together so as to give the typical plastic properties. They have been used with much success in elucidating the reaction between rubber and sulphur, on which vulcanization depends. This process was discovered in 1839, but until recently its chemical mechanism was very obscure.

Radioisotopes have a vast range of applications, in which the sort of radiation emitted is the primary consideration, and the atom emitting it is only of secondary interest. In these applications the radiations could, theoretically, be produced by X-ray tubes or natural radium, but these would be impracticable or too expensive. The radioisotope acts as a constant, compact, relatively cheap source of the desired sort of radiation, which may be used for measuring the thickness of a product, sorting raw materials, detecting internal flaws, etc.

The continuous testing, or monitoring, of the thickness of thin strips of materials used in manufacture, such as cigarette-paper, the thin paper used in making electrical condensers for radio sets, and acetate film for packing purposes, is of great industrial importance. Unless the material utilized by automatic machinery is within narrow limits of size, the machinery may be jammed or stopped. The interruption of automatic production processes is commercially very expensive. The success of mass production depends, therefore, on a constant stream of material of uniform quality being fed to the automatic machines.

α-, β- and γ-rays from radioisotopes have all been applied in various ways in these monitoring processes. The α-rays, which consist of helium nuclei, have the characteristic of being emitted at definite and known speeds. Consequently, when a beam of α-particles is projected through a thin layer of material, all the particles will be slowed down to the same extent. Their loss of speed will be a measure of the thickness of the material. α-particles have only a short range, and are suited for monitoring thin materials such as cigarette-paper. Natural radium, or polonium 210, are among the sources of α-rays used in this type of gauge.

Radioisotopes emitting β-rays, or electrons, are widely used for gauging thicker sheets and strips, produced in the steel, aluminium, plastics, paper, glass, cloth, floor-covering and other industries. Very thick materials may be gauged with the aid of the penetrating γ-rays.

In all these devices, the material measured is not touched or damaged, and the improvement in the control of production often leads to big savings. For instance, the Congoleum-Nairn Corporation which manufactures floor-covering, has found that control by a radioisotope device has reduced deviations from the standard thickness of the product by an average of 56 per cent, and in one case by 87 per cent, giving a more uniform product and more economical use of material.

Radioisotopes are used for controlling the manufacture of glass-fibre insulating sheet. The density is measured continuously by devices which regulate the rate of feed in order to secure a uniform product. Fig. 71 shows the process in operation and Fig. 72 shows the arrangement of the control panel which regulates the feed.

The radiation from a constant source is measured after it has passed through the sheet of material. This gives the thickness. If it has deviated, the feed may be automatically adjusted by a servo-mechanism to bring the thickness back to standard, and if the deviation is beyond the limits of toleration, the piece of defective product may be rejected. Fig. 73 shows an arrangement of this kind for the automatic classification of tin plate. It is reproduced, by permission of the U.S. Atomic Energy Commission, from Conference Paper No. P/164, " The Versatility of Radiation Applications Involving Penetration or Reflection ", by C. E. Crompton.

Radiation methods of measurement, which do not involve contact with the material to be measured, have great advantages for controlling substances such as rubber, which are easily deformed, red-hot products such as steel strip, or sticky substances such as various plastics. Gauges for measuring the thickness of rubber sheet are shown in Fig. 74.

FIG. 71.—MEASURING CONTINUOUSLY THE DENSITY OF GLASS FIBRE INSULATING SHEET.
(Atomic Energy of Canada Limited)

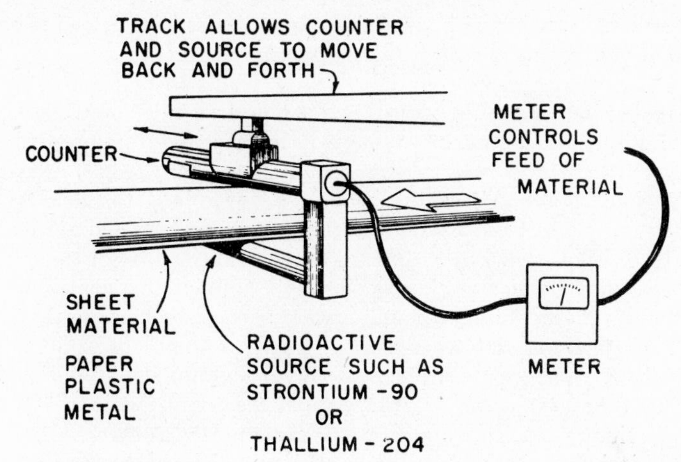

FIG. 72.—THE ARRANGEMENT OF THE CONTROL PANEL WHICH REGULATES THE FEED TO THE MACHINE SHOWN IN FIG. 71.

(*Atomic Energy of Canada Limited*

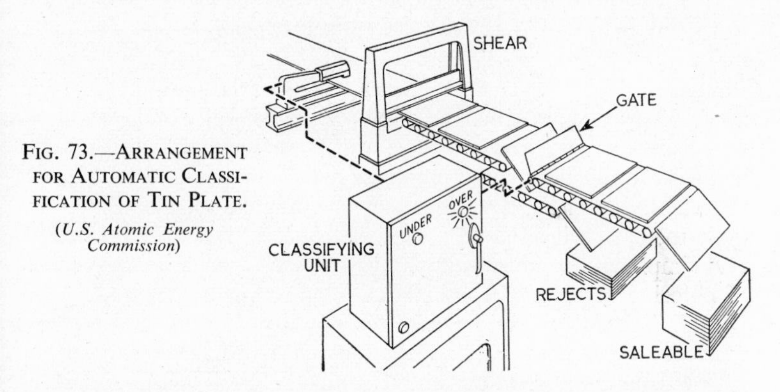

FIG. 73.—ARRANGEMENT FOR AUTOMATIC CLASSIFICATION OF TIN PLATE.

(*U.S. Atomic Energy Commission*)

Messrs. Stewart and Lloyd have used a radioisotope gauge working with γ-rays for measuring the longitudinal thickness profile of the hot metal strip produced in a strip mill, and for gauging hot steel tubes, to test how much they might be out of shape.

The thickness of a flat or curved metal sheet can be determined by measuring the proportion of γ-rays scattered back by the material. One device based on this principle consists of a fine wire of cobalt containing the radioisotope cobalt 60. The wire is half a millimetre in diameter and three millimetres long, and is placed in the pipe or tube parallel to the axis and brought within two-hundredths of an inch of the wall. The device is used for measuring the thickness of pipes in an oil refinery.

Gauges operating with γ-rays have been devised for detecting corrosion in pipes from the outside. This development promises to be very important, for it would allow large plants to be examined for corrosion without being shut down. It is estimated that the successful introduction of this system will increase the total production of such a plant by several per cent.

Various devices have been made for controlling the level of a liquid in a sealed vessel. One group of these devices, elaborated by G. G. Jordan, utilizes the difference in the absorption of γ-rays on the two media which are in contact, say a liquid with a gas above it. A Geiger counter slides up and down a vertical bracket on the side of the sealed vessel. On the other side is a source of radioactive cobalt 60. The radiations pass partly through the liquid and partly through the gas, and it is arranged that the counter is in a state of equilibrium when its centre is at the same height as the level of the liquid inside the vessel. If the level should change, the intensity of the radiation falling on the counter will change, as more or less of it will pass through the gas and liquid respectively. The counter is thrown out of equilibrium, and this is made to start a servo-motor which raises or lowers the counter until it is again in equilibrium at the same level as the liquid.

Such an instrument can keep the level in a large tank to within an accuracy of 5 millimetres. The apparatus will work with tanks 6 yards in diameter, and with steel walls 4 inches thick. It is reliable in action and suitable for completely automatizing technological processes, especially those dealing with aggressive, explosive, and toxic media, such as molten steel in furnaces, liquid chlorine, etc.

A simplified form of this apparatus is used for measuring the level of chlorine in tubular containers.

Radioisotope devices are used for monitoring packages in mass-production processes. The radiation reveals at once whether the package has the correct density of contents. This is a good indication whether it contains the correct number of contents, such as pills. β-ray gauges are used to standardize automatically the packing of the correct quantity of tobacco into cigarettes.

In England experiments have been made for the National Coal Board in which coal was sorted from shale with the aid of radioisotope thulium 170. Coal scatters the low-energy γ-rays from this radioisotope more than shale. As a conventional coal-and-shale separating plant which works on the principle of the difference in density of the two materials costs about £500,000, the development of an inexpensive alternative would be of great economic advantage.

In addition to the ways of using radioisotopes already described, there are many others, based on several principles. One of the most

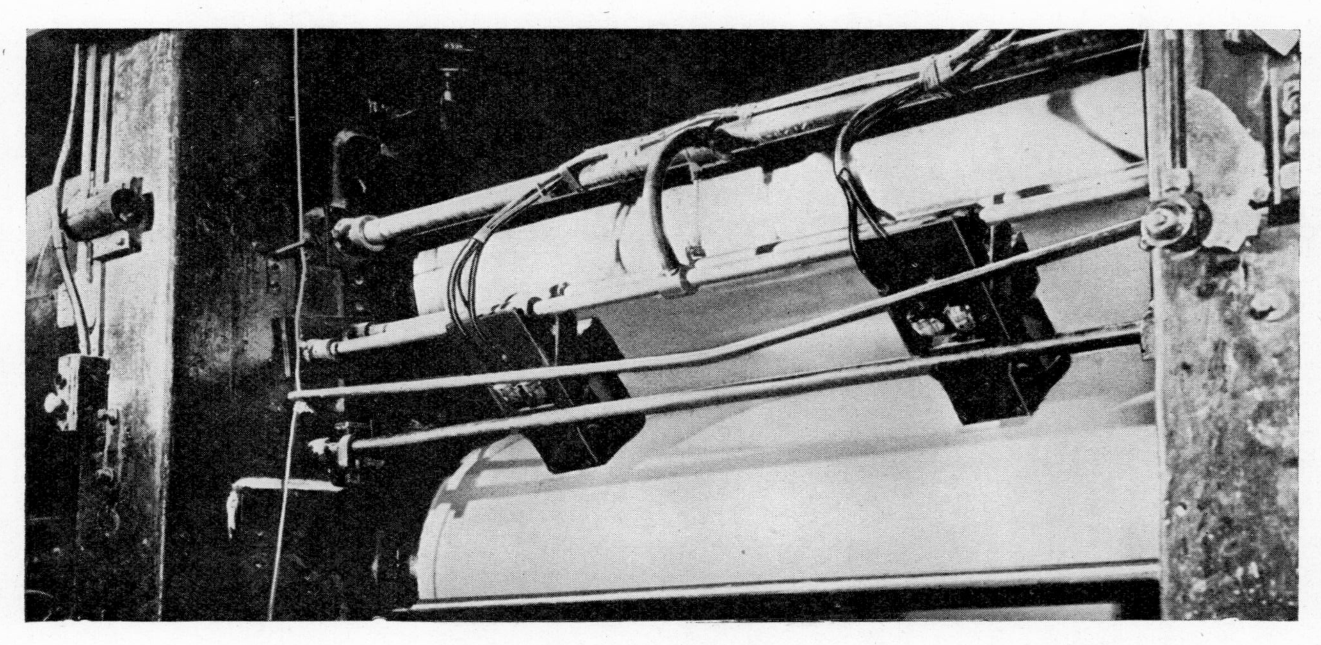

FIG. 74.—RADIOISOTOPIC MEASURING GAUGES MOUNTED TO MEASURE THE THICKNESS OF A RUBBER SHEET.
(U.S. Information Service)

striking is autoradiography. If a radioisotope is incorporated in a mixture such as a plastic preparation, a sample of the product, when laid on a photographic film, will produce a picture of itself. The light and shade of the picture will reveal the intensity of the radiation from the various parts, and whether the material has been properly mixed.

If radioactive tungsten is added to alloys, and the products placed on photographic films, the places where the tungsten has concentrated can be detected. The method is much more sensitive than the conventional etching techniques, and does not damage the specimen.

Autoradiography has proved very effective in measuring the solidification boundary when aluminium is being cast in a continuous process. A small amount of radioactive gold 198 is added to the casting, which is then made to take its picture by autoradiography. The solidification boundary comes out very plainly, as seen in Fig. 75.

The development of radioisotope radiography has extended rapidly. A radioisotope source is used, in effect, as a substitute for X-rays or radium for taking a shadow picture of a solid object, as seen in Fig. 76.

Many small firms which could not have afforded the older expensive equipments, now freely use radioisotope cameras working with cobalt 60, iridium 192, caesium 137 or thulium 170, which would have seemed to them a short time ago to be highly esoteric instruments. As a result, the percentage of faulty metal parts leaving factories and workshops has fallen considerably. An example of a compact γ-ray camera being used to examine a small casting for internal flaws is shown in Fig. 77.

Besides detecting the straying of materials, such as leaking liquids, radioisotopes are used for tracing the exact paths, or geometry, of the movements of materials in space. For instance, some piston rings are designed to rotate as they go up and down in the engine. It is not easy to find out how much they rotate during each stroke. If a quantity of radioisotope is fixed at a spot on the ring, its movement in space can be followed by means of a counter outside the cylinder. In this way, the amount that the ring rotates can be measured.

It is very difficult to find out exactly what happens in the operations on textile fibres. Phosphorus 32 has been used to investigate the changes which occur in the inside of a thread of wool which is being thinned in the process of drafting. The thread is stretched by being run between rollers, the front ones revolving six times as fast as those at the rear, with the effect that the thickness of the

FIG. 75.—A PICTURE OF A TELEPHONE TAKEN WITH THE RADIOISOTOPE GOLD 198.
(*Central Office of Information. Crown Copyright reserved*)

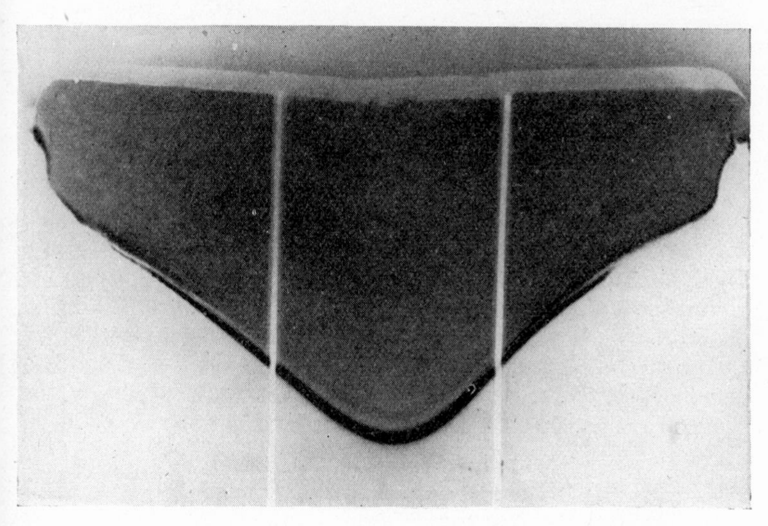

FIG. 76.—RADIOACTIVE GOLD USED FOR DELINEATING THE COOLING BOUNDARY IN AN ALUMINIUM BILLET.
(*United Kingdom Atomic Energy Authority*)

FIG. 77.—OPERATING A "GAMMA CAMERA" TO OBTAIN A RADIOGRAPH OF A CASTING TO DETECT ANY FLAWS.

(*Atomic Energy of Canada Limited*)

thread is reduced by six times. In order to trace the internal changes in the thread, one of its fibres was treated so as to contain phosphorus 32. The radiation from this isotope enabled snapshots of the sequence of positions of the thread to be made, so that its behaviour during the process of thinning could be elucidated.

Some important applications of radioisotopes are based on yet another principle. The radiations from radioisotopes make air and gases conductors of electricity. They are consequently useful as eliminators of electric charges which are built up in manufacturing processes when materials are rubbed together, as in the textile industry and the processing of paper, optical lenses and plastics. These electric charges may produce sparks which might cause explosions. If a suitable radioisotopic source is placed near the region of the charge, it will render the air or gas conductive, so that the charge can leak harmlessly away. By reducing the risk of fire, and thereby enabling the machinery to run faster, the adoption of the devices has in some cases led to an increase of production of 20–50 per cent.

In some textile operations, fibres may become electrified. This causes them to repel each other, and makes hairs stick out, which interfere with the uniformity and smoothness of the product. A radioisotopic source placed near the material in process of manufacture enables these charges to escape, so that fibres remain smooth, and work uniformly together.

The warp threads of certain man-made fibres become charged

(" static ") during weaving or knitting, and may remain so for a considerable time when standing in the loom overnight in dry weather. They then attract to themselves minute particles of dirt from the air which stick so hard that no commercially practicable process can remove them. This " fog-marking " results in considerable wastage of cloth each winter, but can be prevented by hanging small β-sources (e.g. 2 mC of thallium 204) over the loom as soon as weaving stops at night. Fig. 78 shows two similar pieces of nylon fabric warp-knitted with and without the use of the radioactive unit.

Among the radioisotopes used as static eliminators are krypton 85, and tritium. The latter is used for eliminating electric charges when dust is brushed off lenses, and for enabling cathode-ray tubes to start up quickly.

Considerable quantities of radioisotopes are used for making luminous dials on watches and instruments. Formerly, natural radium was chiefly employed, but today this has been largely superseded by polonium 210, which is made in reactors in larger quantities than are obtained from natural sources. Polonium 210 emits α-particles, or helium nuclei. When these impinge on beryllium, they produce streams of neutrons. Mixtures of polonium 210 and beryllium are therefore used as convenient sources of radiation consisting of neutrons, which has advantages for some purposes over

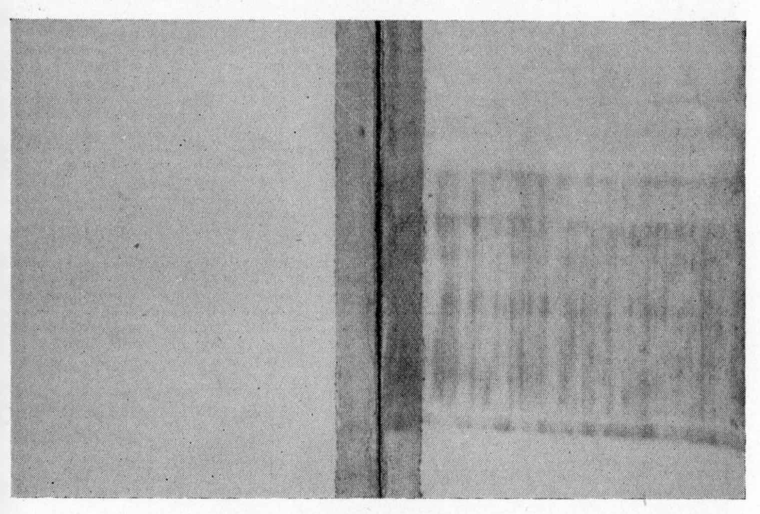

FIG. 78.—CONTRAST BETWEEN TWO SIMILAR PIECES OF NYLON FABRIC WARP-KNITTED WITH AND WITHOUT THE REMOVAL OF STATIC ELECTRIC CHARGE BY A RADIOISOTOPE.

(British Cotton Industry Research Association)

FIG. 79.—WELDED STEEL SEAMS BEING INSPECTED WITH THE AID OF COBALT 60. (*Pantatron Ltd.*)

the other forms of radiation. Neutron sources of this kind are used for logging oil-wells. The neutrons are reflected by the hydrogen in hydrocarbons, and thereby help to reveal the presence of oil.

The only α-emitting radioisotope widely used in industry at present is polonium 210, though in the future no doubt radioisotopic applications will be found for the α-emitting plutonium 239.

The radioisotope cobalt 60 is specially interesting. Ordinary

FIG. 80.—THE U.K. RADIOCHEMICAL CENTRE AT AMERSHAM, BUCKS.
(Central Office of Information. Crown Copyright reserved)

TABLE 10

REACTOR-PRODUCED ISOTOPES EMITTING ELECTRONS

Element	*Isotope*	*Half-life*
Hydrogen	H-3	12·5 years
Carbon	C-14	5,700 „
Phosphorus . . .	P-32	14·3 days
Sulphur.	S-35	87·1 „
Calcium	Ca-45	164 „
Strontium	Sr-90	28 years
Thallium	Tl-204	4 „

TABLE 11

REACTOR-PRODUCED ISOTOPES EMITTING γ-RADIATIONS

Element	*Isotope*	*Half-life*
Sodium	Na-24	14·9 hours
Iron.	Fe-55	2·91 years
Iron.	Fe-59	46·3 days
Cobalt	Co-60	5·3 years
Iodine	I-131	8·05 days
Caesium	Cs-137	33 years
Thulium	Tm-170	127 days
Iridium	Ir-192	74·5 „
Gold	Au-198	2·69 „

stable cobalt can be converted into radioactive sources one hundred times as intense as radium, weight for weight, by placing it in a powerful nuclear reactor for periods of the order of one year. In the process, more than 10 per cent of the stable cobalt is converted into cobalt 60. The cobalt 60 supplies radioactive sources of tremendous power, which are utilized in industry, medicine and scientific research. Fig. 79 shows this radioisotope in use for the inspection of welded seams.

Already, cobalt 60 is produced in reactors in North America at a rate equivalent to more than 200 lb. of natural radium a year. The importance of this development is thrown into vivid relief by the reflection that during the sixty-three years since radium was discovered in 1898, less than 6 lb. have been extracted from the earth by all the radium miners of the world. A new scale of the industrial production of radioactive substances has been established.

Nuclear reactors produce large quantities of radioisotopes as by-products of the fission process. The development of nuclear power will vastly increase this output. They are new materials for industry, and it is desirable to find uses for them, not only to assist established industrial production but to utilize new radioactive material which might otherwise become an accumulating waste, with very embarrassing properties. Special attention is being given to the separation of the useful isotopes such as caesium 137 and strontium 90 from the residues left in the recovery of uranium and plutonium from partially-consumed reactor fuel charges.

The most important radioisotopes produced in nuclear reactors, and which emit electrons, are given in Table 10.

The most important of the reactor-produced isotopes which emit γ-radiations are given in Table 11.

The preparation of radioisotopes for industrial and other applications is carried out in special institutions. In the United Kingdom this work is done at the Radiochemical Centre at Amersham, Bucks. (Fig. 80.)

The applications of radioisotopes in industry are already various, and they will extend very much in the future. They are the biggest practical contribution of nuclear energy to human welfare so far, but although the advances in innumerable directions due to radioisotopes make a most impressive total, it must be said that they have not yet led to any single advance or discovery of an absolutely major order.

Even so great a development as the application of radioisotopes to date is, compared with nuclear power, of secondary importance.

CHAPTER VI

WINNING URANIUM

URANIUM WAS DISCOVERED in 1789, but until the 1940's it was regarded as a rather rare metal. It was used in the pottery industry, and was sought as a guide to the location of the very rare and valuable radium. It was regarded industrially as not very interesting, and the small supplies required were provided as by-products in the commercial extraction of radium and vanadium.

The release of atomic energy suddenly created an intense industrial demand for uranium. Within a very short time knowledge of the content of uranium in the earth, and methods of finding and working it, and even of how it came to be created and distributed in the cosmos, were revolutionized.

Formerly, the methods of prospecting for uranium were exceedingly crude. Only three or four important uranium mines existed in the world. But when it was changed from a minor by-product into a major primary product, the development of special techniques for discovering it became worth while, irrespective of whether they led to the discovery of any other valuable minerals.

Thousands of prospectors, including geologists, geochemists, botanists and geophysicists, entered into the search. They have shown that uranium is a remarkably widespread element, occurring in most of the major geological formations, and must no longer be classed as a rare element. But, compared with the total amount of uranium in the earth, the number of deposits rich in uranium, such as those consisting of the mineral pitchblende, appear to be relatively few. It was the rarity of rich deposits, and the lack of interest in the low concentration of uranium in common rocks, which prevented the magnitude of the uranium content of the earth from being recognized.

The original distribution of uranium in the rocks probably arose from the processes of solution and crystallization occurring when the rocks were molten. Some of these processes increased the concentration in certain regions of the molten material. Consequently, when these solidified, forming rocks such as granite, they contained more uranium than the average.

The quantity of granite is enormous. On the average, it contains four parts per million of uranium, and twelve parts per million of thorium. As the quantity of granite is so large, the total amount of uranium and thorium, though present in low concentration, is, from the industrial point of view, very large. The uranium and thorium can be extracted by technically simple processes of leaching with dilute acid. Harrison Brown has shown that the amount which can be easily leached from one ton of granite is sufficient to produce nuclear energy equivalent to the burning of about ten tons of coal. But the amount of energy required to process and leach the ton of granite would be equivalent to that obtained by burning only 50 lb. of coal. Hence, on balance there would be a big gain in energy by processing and leaching granite for uranium and thorium. At present, however, this would not be economic.

The utilization of these virtually unlimited low-grade uranium and thorium resources belongs to the future. But the knowledge that they exist enables the development of nuclear energy to proceed with great confidence, and it indicates that in mining as in numerous other directions, immense developments are in prospect.

In various rocks veins are occasionally found in which there are lumps of the black, sooty-looking mineral pitchblende. This may contain from 1 per cent to almost pure uranium oxide. The discovery of radium in pitchblende stimulated the interest of prospectors in this mineral.

Uranium was first mined on a considerable scale from rich pitchblende deposits, but very few of these were of considerable extent. One of the most famous is in the great mineral field of Central Africa, which contains the mines of the Congo and Rhodesia. The small but very rich mine of Shinkolobwe has produced more uranium than any other ore-field so far. In the Congo-Rhodesia area uranium is associated with copper and cobalt. It is estimated that 100 million tons of copper and one million tons of cobalt are obtainable from this area. Already, during the post-war decade 1945–54, £639 million worth of minerals were mined from the Rhodesias alone, and now the prospects for uranium mining seem promising.

One of the biggest developments of uranium mining has taken place in Canada. More persons are searching there now for uranium than for any other metal, and large discoveries have been made.

After Canada was first occupied by Europeans, it was for long a fur-trading country inhabited by Red Indians and trappers. Mining began with the gold rush of 1858, and prospectors adopted the methods of their predecessors in moving about the country. Ordinary prospecting is done on foot. Local travel is usually by canoe, now powered by outboard motors. Aircraft with floats are used to carry men and equipment, including canoes, to desired regions. Limited use is being made of helicopters, and of the dropping of supplies by parachute.

The basic discovery of uranium deposits arose out of routine work by the Geological Survey of Canada. In 1900 the Survey sent J. M. Bell, then 23 years old, to explore Great Bear Lake. At the end of the summer Bell and his assistants moved to the shore of the east end of the lake to find Red Indian guides who would lead them south before winter set in. Bell noted in his report of 1901 to the Survey that the steep rocky shores of the lake were often stained with cobalt bloom and copper green.

In 1929, when aircraft were beginning to revolutionize the transport of prospecting, an experienced prospector, G. A. La Bine, decided to use the new means for exploring Great Bear Lake. He was aware of Bell's observation of cobalt and copper blooms, and set out to rediscover them in the hope that they might indicate the presence of valuable deposits of silver and copper. He landed beside the lake while it was still frozen, with 1,600 lb. of supplies, and the intention of spending the summer exploring 500 miles of the lake's shores. By the middle of May, however, he noticed a great wall of rock stained with cobalt and copper green. He investigated the place carefully, and found cobalt and its associated ores, and while continuing the search, he found a piece of dark ore of about the size of a large plum. He searched for the vein from whence it had come, found it, and chipped a piece off. He recognized it to be pitchblende.

As the price of radium was then $2 million an ounce, La Bine's mining company decided to work the deposit. The mine, called Port Radium, only 25 miles from the Arctic Circle, and 1,355 miles by boat from the nearest railhead, began to produce in 1933, and in 1936 the first ounce of radium was processed. Besides radium, the mine produced as by-products silver, uranium, copper and cobalt. In 1940, owing to the disruption of the radium market by the Second World War, the mine was closed down. Then, in 1942, when the release of nuclear energy by uranium fission promised to be successful, the company was requested to resume operations, now with the aim of primarily producing uranium. In 1943, the company was taken over by the Canadian Government under the title of Eldorado Mining and Refining Limited. Port Radium (Fig. 81) was developed, and intense prospecting for uranium was pursued over Canada. In four years, 1,000 new radioactive occurrences were discovered.

These were found mainly along the edge of the Canadian Shield, the vast arc of rocks resembling those of Scandinavia, which enclose Hudson Bay and cover about one-half of the country (see Fig. 82). The most important was at Beaverlodge Lake. A geological fault was discovered, 6½ miles long, containing the Ace, Fay, Eagle, Verna, Martin and several other deposits. The region is inaccessible except

Fig. 81.—Port Radium, Northwest Territories.

(Nationa Film Board, Ottawa)

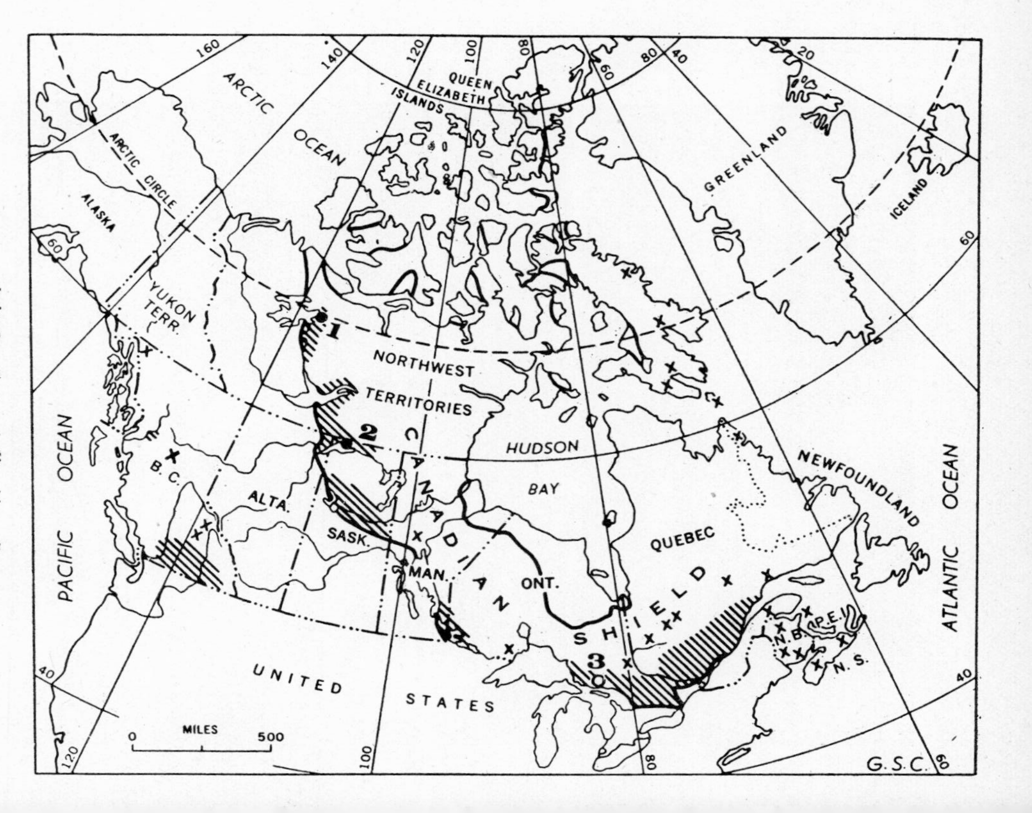

FIG. 82.—CANADIAN URANIUM AREAS.

Area containing one or more producing mines: 1, Great Bear Lake; 2, Beaverlodge . ●

Area to be in production late in 1955: 3, Blind River . ○

Area containing several occurrences . . . (hatched)

Isolated occurrence . . . ×

Compiled by Geological Survey of Canada (Atomic Energy of Canada Limited) by air for eight months of the year. The Ace-Fay mines (Fig. 83) were already treating 700 tons of ore per day in 1955.

The Gunnar Mines Limited, whose president is G. A. La Bine, has a deposit in the neighbourhood of Beaverlodge Lake, estimated to be worth $130 million, and has built a plant for treating 1,250 tons of ore per day.

In the Blind River region of Ontario, on the north shore of Lake Huron, various mines with deposits valued at more than $370 million have erected plants for treating 7,250 tons of ore per day.

The Port Radium and Beaverlodge mines are served by a transportation company which operates 23 tugs and 66 barges. Figs. 84 and 85 illustrate the activities of this company.

The boats can operate for only three to four months in the year. In the winter the average temperature at Port Radium is – 20° C., and it frequently falls to – 40° C., below the freezing-point of mercury. During the winter months the mines are supplied by air.

The concentrates from the mines are sent to a refinery at Port Hope, and thence to the United States for the final extraction of the metal. The concentrates from Port Radium travel 3,731 miles to the refinery at Port Hope.

When uranium became a major commodity, it became worth while to develop special methods for prospecting for it. These primarily depend on the utilization of the property that distinguishes

FIG. 83.—THE HEADFRAME OF THE FIVE-COMPARTMENT SHAFT OF THE ACE-FAY MINE.

(*Atomic Energy of Canada Limited*)

FIG. 84.—THE 297-TON " RADIUM GILBERT " BRINGS A BARGE INTO PORT RADIUM, AFTER CROSSING GREAT BEAR LAKE.

(*Atomic Energy of Canada Limited*)

FIG. 85.—THE " RADIUM KING " PUSHES BARGES THROUGH THE ICE ON GREAT SLAVE LAKE.

(*Atomic Energy of Canada Limited*)

it from other minerals, i.e. its radioactivity. The new major discoveries of uranium have been made mainly through prospecting for radioactivity. This is carried out in many ways. Individual prospectors carry counters with them on the ground, note the radioactivity in the neighbourhood and of the materials which they collect

FIG. 86.—MEASURING RADIOACTIVITY FROM THE GROUND WITH A SCINTILLATING COUNTER.
(*The Radiac Company Inc.*)

(see Figs. 86 and 87). The interpretation of the value of the observations is generally not easy, and the various government geological surveys have received large numbers of excited communications from prospectors who have detected some radioactivity. These have been investigated with much patience, in the hope that they might lead to valuable discoveries. But the systematic examination for radioactivity of the specimens in the collection of minerals in geological museums has been more fruitful. The origin and geological disposition of these specimens has usually been thoroughly studied, so the general significance, for a region, of the discovery of radioactivity in a specimen from it, can be deduced with more certainty.

The most effective prospecting is, however, now done by teams of experienced prospectors and scientists, furnished with elaborate equipment. The most important particular equipment consists of very sensitive radioactive detectors, especially scintillation counters, carried by aircraft. These are one of the oldest types of instrument for detecting radiations, and were used by Crookes and Rutherford in their classical experiments. They consist of crystals of various kinds, which produce flashes of light when radiations strike them. The early investigators counted the scintillations by eye. Since those days, the instrument has been greatly developed. New kinds of sensitive crystal have been discovered, and photo-electric cells are used for detecting and counting the scintillations. By electronic devices, the sensitivity of the photo-electric counting system can be increased millions of times, and the recording made automatic.

The modern scintillation counter may be up to one hundred times as sensitive as a Geiger counter, which depends on the ionization or electrification of air or gas. An example of a scintillation detector for aerial prospecting is shown in Fig. 88. The complete equipment weighs about 17 lb. The sensitive crystal consists of radium iodide, which is activated by thallium. It is 3 inches long and $1\frac{1}{2}$ inches thick. The radioactivity is recorded by a pen on a moving strip, and an automatic alarm warns the pilot whenever he is passing over an anomaly, so that he can give close attention to flying his plane in the right path.

The development of the counter for detecting radioactive deposits has now led to its widespread application in prospecting for other

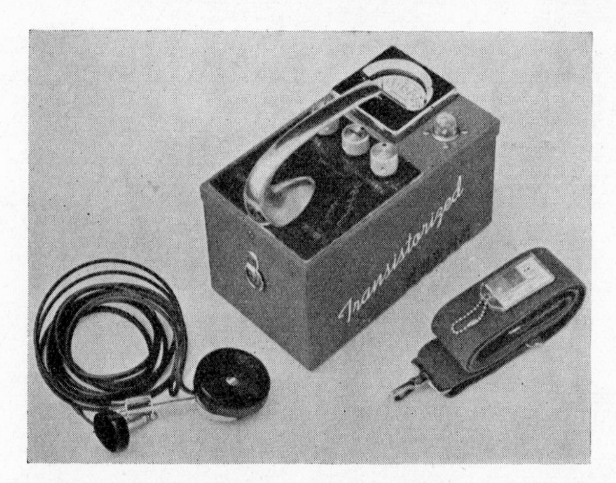

FIG. 87.—A TRANSISTORIZED GEIGER COUNTER FOR DETECTING RADIOACTIVE MINERALS.

(*The Radiac Company Inc.*)

FIG. 88.—SCINTILLATION DETECTOR DESIGNED FOR ONE-MAN PILOT DETECTORS.
(*The Radiac Company Inc.*)

minerals. As small quantities of uranium are often associated with petroleum, diamonds, gold, silver, copper and other metals, the search for the associated uranium is pursued as a clue to these minerals. Indeed, in 1953, one maker of scintillation detectors sold more of these instruments for petroleum than for uranium prospecting. This is an example of how the demand for fuel for nuclear energy has stimulated the improvement of equipment, which has then improved technique, and found profitable applications, in quite other directions.

The most effective way of making a general radioactive survey of vast countries such as Canada, the U.S.S.R. or Brazil, is to fly over large areas according to a systematic pattern. The most effective height is about 200 feet, and the limit of useful observations is at about 500 feet.

The average radioactivity over broad areas can be determined, and its equivalent in radium content can be calculated within a few thousandths of one per cent. Promising regions are noted for more detailed investigations. These are undertaken with light single-engine aircraft, flying at 50 to 100 feet above the ground, at speeds of about 60 m.p.h. The method is most effective where favourable formations are known to exist, and is especially effective where the favourable strata are horizontal, and exposed from time to time in vertical cliffs. The aircraft is flown within 100 feet of the cliffs, following the contour of the outcropping strata. The contrast between the record of a significant radiation observation and that of the ordinary background of radiation is five times as great on an

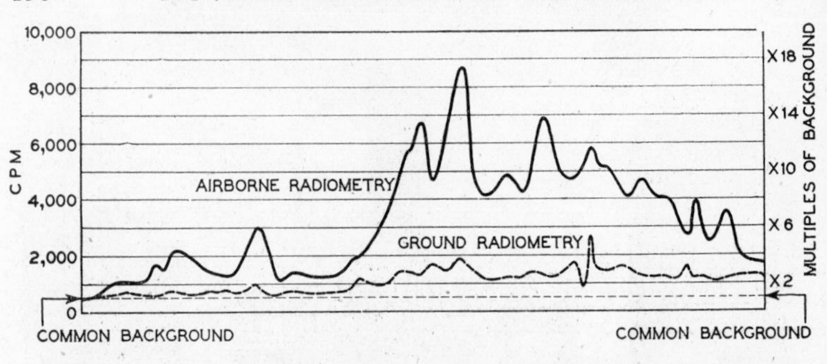

FIG. 89.—COMPARISON OF AIRBORNE AND GROUND RADIOMETRIC PROFILES.
(*D. A. MacFadyen and Silvio V. Guedes*)

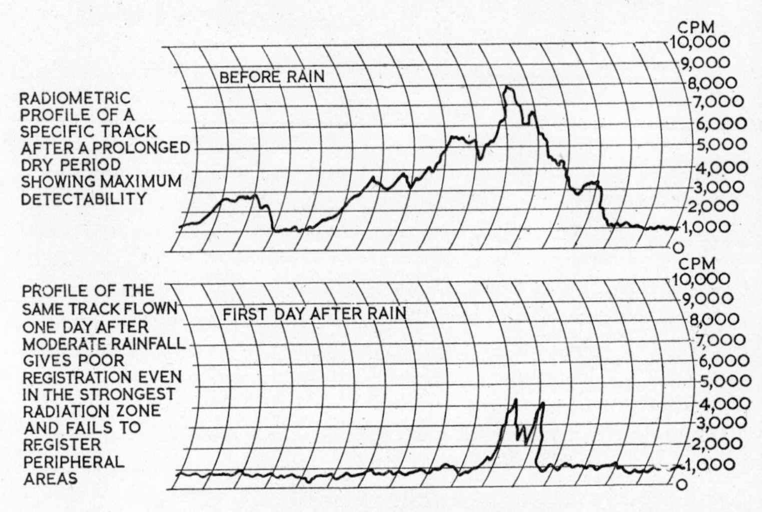

FIG. 90.—EFFECT OF HUMIDITY IN AIRBORNE ACTIVITY. RECORDINGS OF RADIOACTIVITY BEFORE AND AFTER RAIN.
(*D. A. MacFadyen and Silvio V. Guedes*)

airborne counter as on one on the surface of the ground, as shown diagrammatically in Fig. 89.

Careful attention must be paid to the weather. If the air is wet and humid, much radiation escapes, and low recordings may be obtained even from areas which are strongly radioactive. Fig. 90 shows comparative recordings before and after rain.

The power of prospecting with airborne scintillation counters is illustrated by the map of the well-known thorium monazite deposits on the Brazilian coast, published by D. A. MacFadyen and S. V. Guedes. The airborne counters located and outlined all the known

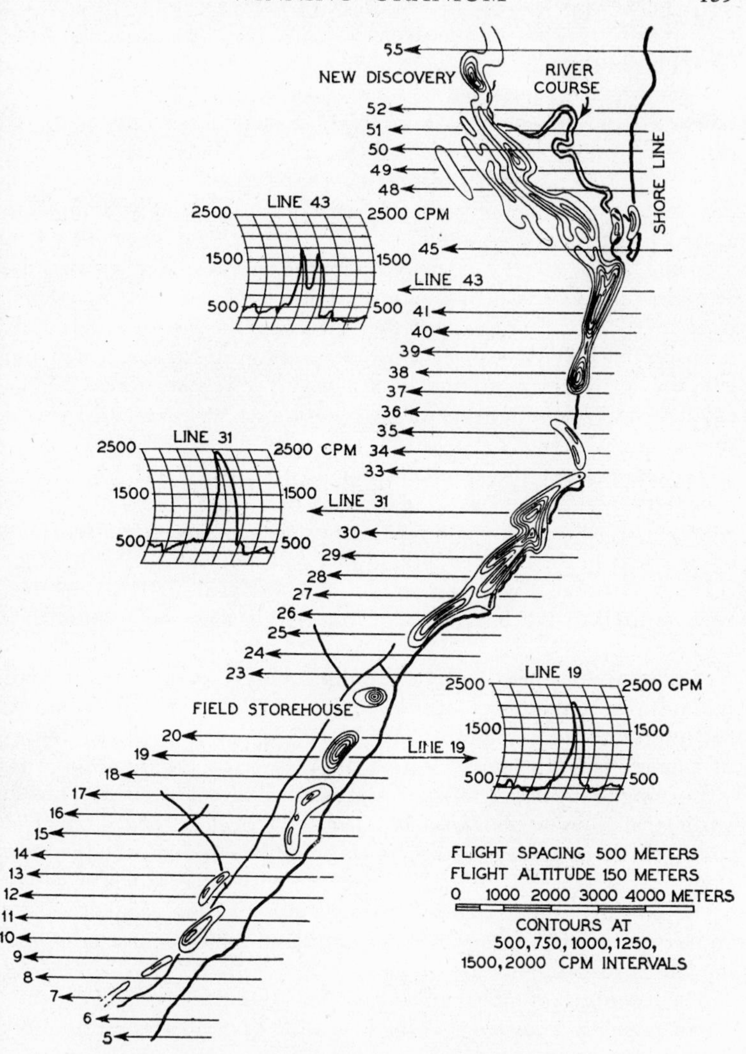

FIG. 91.—AIRBORNE RADIOMETRY OF MONAZITE DEPOSITS ON THE BRAZILIAN COAST.

(*D. A. MacFadyen and Silvio V. Guedes*)

deposits, and registered intensities in remarkably accurate proportion to the known quantities of monazite lying about 3 feet below the surface (see Fig. 91). In addition, they indicated the existence of a completely unknown deposit within a short distance of an area which had been intensively prospected on the ground. The survey was so sensitive that it even detected some bags of radioactive concentrate which had been stored in a hut.

The Brazilian radioactive surveys made by MacFadyen and Guedes, from which items have been quoted here, were made by one organization in eighteen months. Incidentally, deposits of an associated mineral, valued at five thousand times the whole cost of the eighteen months' operations in the air and on the ground, were also discovered.

In the U.S.S.R. very extensive airborne surveys have been made, and several deposits of industrial importance have been discovered by them. In addition to the other methods, the Soviet prospectors have particularly developed those depending on the chemistry and geology of waters migrating in the earth. They are based on the fundamental scientific work of the geochemist V. I. Vernadsky, and the geologist A. E. Fersman.

Vernadsky was the founder of a distinguished school of geochemistry, and as early as 1922 forecast that " the time is not far off when man will obtain control of atomic energy . . . This may come about in the next few years, or it may not happen for another century, but that it will happen is now quite clear." His work has been utilized in the Soviet Union for the location of uranium ore bodies.

All natural waters contain uranium, from about one-hundred-millionth of a gram per litre in the waters from barren rocks, to two-millionths of a gram per litre in the sea, and several hundredths of a gram per litre in the waters draining from uranium deposits. Accordingly, in this method of prospecting, samples of waters from springs, streams, wells and drill holes are collected, their content of radioactive substances is determined, and the results obtained are then interpreted. If the radioactive content of the waters is found to be unusually high, a more detailed investigation is made of the sources from whence they came, and the other methods of prospecting are also brought into play.

The technique of interpretation is highly complicated, and depends on an extensive knowledge of the migration of radioactive substances dissolved in underground waters in the normal geological formations. By comparing the facts in any particular case with this general background of knowledge, significant anomalies may be recognized. Besides establishing the background for each kind of rock, it is necessary also to work out the effect of climate and seasons of the year. The waters from rock in a dry climate may contain much more uranium than those from similar rock in a wet climate, and yet the observation may not be significant, as the concentration may be due to evaporation of water from the surface soil.

FIG. 92.—URANIUM COUNTRY OF THE WESTERN UNITED STATES.
The wild canyons of the Colorado Plateau cover an area of 110,000 square miles.
(U.S. Information Service)

These detailed chemical and geological studies of migratory waters have provided an effective method of uranium prospecting which has led in the Soviet Union to the discovery of new ore-bearing districts, as well as new ore bodies in deposits already being mined or prospected.

The principal source of uranium in the United States is at present sandstones, mudstones and limestones, in which uranium minerals such as carnotite occur as fillings and impregnations in pores. Thirty-seven of these sedimentary deposits have yielded uranium, and eighteen have furnished at least 1,000 tons of ore with an average content of more than 0·1 per cent of uranium oxide. In most of these ores, there is from one to twenty times as much vanadium oxide.

Very extensive prospecting for uranium has been carried out in the United States; $46 million has already been spent on it, and a further $12 million on metallurgical research on the treatment of uranium and allied problems. Besides the richer deposits such as those found in the Western States (Fig. 92), there are vast quantities of low-grade ores. An interesting example of these is the phosphate rocks of Florida. These contain 0·01 per cent of uranium oxide. They are mined on a big scale as material for phosphate fertilizers. As the sale of the fertilizer covers the cost of the mining and preliminary treatment, these expensive operations need not be included in the cost of uranium extracted as a by-product. Consequently, the cost of uranium from this low-grade ore is not as high as might be expected.

In the manufacture of the fertilizer, the phosphate is treated with sulphuric acid, and phosphoric acid is formed. The uranium compounds dissolve in the phosphoric acid, and can be separated from it by solvent extraction. The process has been installed in full-scale plants, and produces uranium at a cost which competes with that from sources of higher grade.

The recovery of uranium as a by-product is being conducted by the South African gold-mining industry on a big scale. The presence of uranium in the gold ores of the Witwatersrand was noted in 1922, but no interest was taken in this until 1941, when the demand for uranium for nuclear energy excited enquiries into the amount of, and the possibilities of extracting, uranium. In 1945, it was reported that the Rand might prove to be one of the largest fields of low-grade uranium ore in the world. Uranium was in fact many times more plentiful than gold in the Witwatersrand ores. Ore from every gold-mine and borehole was examined for radioactivity, and more than 400,000 samples were tested with Geiger counters.

Comprehensive plans were made for developing the uranium

FIG. 93.—YELLOW-WHITE MINEDUMPS AT JOHANNESBURG.
Uranium Ore has been found in dumps like these.

(South African Bureau of Information)

production from the most promising mines, and by April 1955 twenty mining companies were supplying ore to eleven uranium plants. At a number of mines there are vast accumulations of " waste ", left over from previous gold-mining operations (see Fig. 93). These have become a valuable source of uranium, which is being extracted from them by suitable treatment.

The process of uranium extraction is basically similar to that employed in the recovery of gold. The residue left after the extraction of the gold is treated with sulphuric acid. The uranium is dissolved, and the powdered rock in the form of slime is filtered from the solution containing the uranium. It is a technically difficult operation which is assisted by adding quantities of liquid glue.

One uranium plant costs about £3 million, and consumes large quantities of chemical reagents. South Africa already has eleven, and will have fifteen by April 1956. In 1955 the uranium plants were using each month:

Sulphuric acid	39,000	tons
Lime	15,000	,,
Limestone	10,000	,,
Manganese ore	18,000	,,
Solid glue	400	,,

Electricity was consumed at the rate of 77,000 kilowatts, and water at the rate of 300 million gallons per month. When this uranium production was started, no sulphuric acid was available. Consequently, additional South African sulphuric acid plants were built to meet the demand. These were the first plants in the world to use fluo-solid roasters.

The cost of mining and milling the uranium ore is usually debited against the cost of the gold production. As long as gold is extracted from these ores, it will certainly be worth while to extract the uranium. And perhaps in the future it may become more worth while to extract the uranium than the gold.

In India, the monazite sands on the coasts of Malabar and Coromandel are of outstanding importance. They contain at least 180,000 tons of thorium, and are a resource to which India can look for a substantial rise in her low material standard of life. These sands extend below the tide-mark and are continually replenished by fresh supplies washed in by the Indian Ocean from the continental shelf.

The winning of uranium and thorium presents a magnificent prospect of immense and varied development, involving new and intense studies of the contents and structure of the earth, and the application of many branches of science and engineering.

CHAPTER VII

THE NEW METALLURGY AND TECHNOLOGY

As uranium is the sole basic nuclear fuel, and is usually consumed in the metallic state, nuclear engineering has required the development of a new branch of technology: the preparation and treatment of metallic fuels. The conventional fuels, such as coal and oil, are non-metallic, and their life in the furnace is brief. Consequently, their structural properties while burning are not very important. It does not matter much, for the purpose of combustion, whether they are brittle solids or viscous liquids. These qualities are more important outside than inside the furnace, for they affect the ease with which the conventional fuels, which are consumed in very large quantities, can be transported.

The requirements of metallic uranium as a nuclear fuel are quite different. As relatively little is needed, its qualities for ease of transport are unimportant. In the nuclear reactor it is consumed slowly, and may last for months. It must preserve its shape, so that the nuclear chain-reaction can proceed satisfactorily during that period, under the strange conditions of intense radioactive radiation. The metallurgist is confronted with the problem of fabricating metal fuel elements which will withstand these novel conditions, and he must find the solution solely in terms of uranium. He cannot choose from a range of metals the one that would be the easiest to work.

It happens that the particular metal he is compelled to use is one of the most difficult and temperamental. First of all, it is radioactive. The activity from quantities in bulk is considerable, and presents hazards to health, which must be guarded against. It is very dense, being about nineteen times as dense as water. It is chemically very active both when solid and when molten. It reacts easily with the atmosphere, with water, and with crucible linings. These properties make it difficult to melt, cast and fabricate.

In Britain, the smelting of the uranium is carried out at the United Kingdom Atomic Energy Authority's works at Springfields, near Preston (Fig. 94). As slight impurities in the uranium may absorb neutrons, and interfere with the fission chain-reaction, the product must be exceptionally pure.

The ore arrives at Springfields in drums. It consists of powder and lumps. Care is taken to remove any radioactive radon gas which may have been emitted from disintegrating uranium, through

FIG. 94.—A PART OF THE CRUDE URANIUM OXIDE PLANT AT SPRINGFIELDS, PRESTON.

(Reproduced from "Britain's Atomic Factories", by permission of the Controller, H.M. Stationery Office. Crown Copyright reserved)

a ventilating system. Wet methods of treatment are extensively used, in order to reduce the hazard of the inhaling of the radioactive dust by the workmen.

As the nuclear energy industry presents many kinds of hazards to the health of workers, stringent precautions are necessary. Experience has shown that, so far, the direct occupational danger for workers in the industry appears to be less than half that in other comparable industries. Sir John Cockcroft has remarked that the danger from accidents on the roads outside the Atomic Energy Research Establishment at Harwell is far greater than the danger from nuclear energy inside the Establishment.

Professor D. I. Blokhintsev of the U.S.S.R. has expressed the opinion that work in atomic energy installations is safe, provided that precautions are carried out with strict discipline.

FIG. 95.—DEMONSTRATING THE MANIPULATION OF REMOTE CONTROL TONGS FOR HANDLING HIGHLY RADIOACTIVE MATERIALS.
(United Nations Organization)

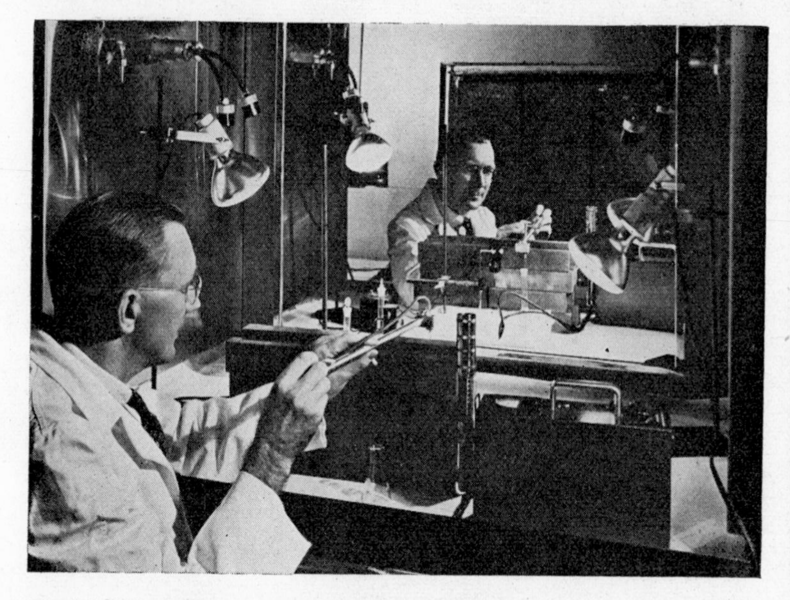

FIG. 96.—THE SCIENTIST, AIDED BY A MIRROR AND WORKING BEHIND A PROTECTIVE SHIELD OF LEAD BLOCKS, IS DILUTING A SOLUTION OF RADIOACTIVE STRONTIUM CHLORIDE, FOR EXPERIMENTAL USE.

(*Bell Telephone Laboratories*)

Dr. H. J. Bhabha has pointed out that the direct biological effects of radiation are fairly well known, and it is possible to prescribe safe tolerance doses, though even on this there appears to be some divergence of view among experts. But not enough is known about indirect effects, especially on the genetics of human beings, animals and plants, and it is imperative that the exact nature of the long-range genetic effects of a small rise in the general level of radiation should be established beyond doubt, so that adequate measures to avoid any ill-effects can be taken. Bhabha has expressed the opinion that the extra careful and conservative precautions which have so far been observed have prevented any serious radiation dangers arising from the peaceful programme of atomic energy development.

Human beings have been exposed for thousands of years to the natural radioactivity on the surface of the earth and the cosmic rays. This has not led to any disaster, so provided the additional radioactivity let into the air or sea is strictly controlled, and kept down to a low level, peaceful atomic development would seem to be safe. The United Nations has begun a study of the effects of radioactive radiation, which will no doubt contribute to the drafting of international regulations dealing with atomic radiation hazards.

The protection of men and women working in atomic factories is ensured by many precautions. The dangerous material is kept at a safe distance, and if necessary surrounded by blankets of lead or concrete to stop the radiations, and is handled indirectly by remote-control equipment (see Figs. 95 and 96). Particular care is needed to prevent the breathing of radioactive dust. This can be prevented by adequate filtering of the air, ventilation and, if necessary, the wearing of protective clothing (Fig. 97).

Elaborate washing, bathing and changing of clothes is adopted,

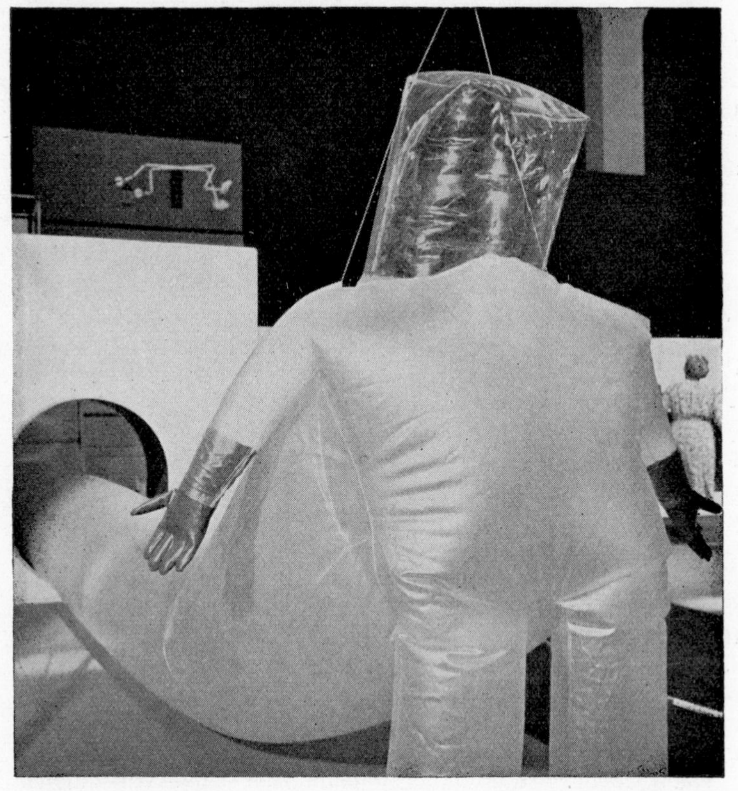

FIG. 97.—A PLASTIC SUIT WORN BY TECHNICIANS WORKING IN HIGHLY RADIO-ACTIVE PLACES.

It is entered from an adjacent room, through the plastic tunnel. Such suits may be useful in dealing with dangerous escapes of radioactive material owing to breakdowns and accidents.

(*United Nations Organization*)

and eating and smoking in dangerous places is prohibited. The health of the staff is kept under constant observation by regular medical examination.

Instruments for keeping a continuous record of the intensity of radiation are set up in key places, both inside and outside the works. Every worker carries such a monitoring instrument in his pocket. This continuously and automatically registers the amount of radiation he is receiving. One type is called a " fountain-pen " monitor, because it can be carried in the pocket like a fountain-pen. It contains a small chamber of air, with a delicate metal-coated quartz fibre. The radiation ionizes, or electrifies, the air and the total amount of radiation is indicated by the movement of the fibre.

Returning to the extraction of uranium, the crushed ore is made into a slurry with water, and stirred with nitric and sulphuric acids. Radium and other precious metals are precipitated, and then the uranium is precipitated as uranium peroxide. The uranium peroxide is converted into uranyl nitrate by solution in warm nitric acid. The uranyl nitrate solution is purified by treatment with ether, and the uranium is precipitated with ammonia as ammonium diuranate.

This is converted into uranium tetrafluoride in three stages, first by heating in an electric furnace, then reducing with hydrogen, and finally with hydrofluoric acid gas (see Fig. 98).

The uranium metal is extracted from the tetrafluoride by a reaction with calcium metal in a mould lined with calcium fluoride, and filled with the inert gas argon. The reaction is started by dropping an ignited pellet of potassium nitrate and lactose into the charge. Much heat is generated, and the metal runs to the bottom of the mould, where it solidifies into a billet, and the calcium fluoride from the reaction floats on the top as a slag.

Owing to urgency, this complicated process was worked out and used successfully on the industrial scale without being tried on the intermediate pilot plant scale. It is a classic example of how, by thorough scientific and technical analysis, extensive and time-consuming work with pilot plants may be cut out in industrial development, even with advantage, since it eliminates the possibility of the design perpetuating faults arising from the provisional character of the pilot plant.

The behaviour of a crystal of uranium metal is markedly different along its three axes. When its temperature is varied it expands along two of the axes but contracts along the third. Consequently, the properties of an ordinary piece of uranium are greatly affected by treatment such as rolling, which changes the orientation of its constituent crystals.

FIG. 98.—THREE FORMS OF URANIUM CONCENTRATE.

(*Left*) Brown Uranium Oxide.
(*Upper Right*) Uranium Tetrafluoride.
(*Lower Right*) Orange Uranium Oxide.

(*Union Carbide International Company*)

It exists in three crystalline forms, changing from the first to the second at 670° C., and from the second to the third at 760° C. In the first forms, the metal is soft and ductile, in the second it is hard and brittle, and in the third it is too soft to be fabricated.

In spite of all these difficulties, uranium is now successfully fabricated by forging, rolling, swaging and drawing, into various shapes and thicknesses of plates, foil, rods, wires and tubes. Satisfactory methods of machining have been worked out. It is advisable to use heavy cuts and high speeds, and a suitable lubricant.

The metal must be protected from the atmosphere in hot-working and in annealing.

Arising from its peculiar crystalline structure, uranium has some startling properties. If a rod in the first form, existing below 670° C., is alternately heated and cooled, it begins to grow. The growth is cumulative, and may amount to six times the original length.

In a nuclear reactor, the variations in temperature may cause the uranium to grow. In some instances, when the uranium is alloyed with small quantities of other metals, this effect is increased.

The intense irradiation in the reactor produces even more startling effects. A piece of uranium may be elongated to one hundred times its original length. Its strength is markedly reduced, and it becomes harder and less ductile. The fragments from fissions accumulate inside, and increase its volume. Nevertheless, the observed increase in volume is twice as great as can be accounted for in this way.

It is not surprising that such changes should occur. The big fragments that fly out of nuclear fissions have enormous energy and bash the normal arrangement of atoms in the metal with terrific force. The atomic structure becomes severely distorted, and the effects become manifest through big external changes.

The metallurgist tries to take advantage of the unequal growth along the three axes of the uranium crystals, and arrange that the assemblage of crystals in the uranium of his fuel elements are orientated in such a way that growth in unwanted directions is eliminated or reduced. This can be done to some extent by suitable heat treatment and rolling, which causes the constituent crystals to line up, and acquire desired orientations.

The resistance of the uranium to irradiation growth is also increased by alloying with small amounts of chromium, niobium, molybdenum or zirconium.

Resistance to corrosion by water is particularly important, owing to the use of water as a cooling medium and moderator in many reactors. It is increased by suitable heat treatment, and by alloying with small amounts of zirconium, molybdenum, niobium or silicon.

But the chemical reactivity of uranium is so great that the metal has usually to be clad in a case of more resistant metal, which, however, must not interfere too much with the nuclear chain-reaction by absorbing many neutrons. The metal cladding may be unbonded, or bonded to the uranium by brazing or rolling. Metals that have been used for cladding include aluminium and stainless steel, but the most promising is zirconium, because of its resistance to corrosion, strength and relatively low appetite for neutrons.

Many metals which were hitherto believed to be rare are now found to be quite common. They seemed to be rare mainly because they were chemically difficult, and were not sought for. The search inspired by the nuclear industrial demand has indirectly influenced the theory of the distribution of elements in the earth and the cosmos, through providing more exact information on how much of the various kinds are in the earth. Incidentally, it has altered the perspective of the natural resources of the earth, for it is now being learned that some of the familiar industrial metals, the known resources of which are very small, may possibly be replaced in the future by other metals that hitherto were believed to be esoteric substances and intractable rarities.

Thorium can be converted into the fissile uranium 233 by neutrons from, for example, uranium 235. J. V. Dunworth has calculated that if thorium could be used up completely in reactors, 15 tons could provide the fuel for the whole of the British electricity supply. In practice, at least 1,000 tons of thorium per annum would be needed if all the new electricity power stations were fuelled with thorium. However, as soon as thorium becomes available in tens of tons, it could be used on an appreciable scale in Britain. The thorium would have to be put into a uranium reactor suitable for converting it into uranium 233, and remain there for a long time before a substantial fraction was converted. Consequently, a considerable quantity of thorium would be required to obtain an appreciable amount of uranium 233 in a reasonable time.

As it is a less difficult metal than uranium metallurgically and chemically, it may for these and other reasons become an even more valuable fuel than uranium.

The invention by Welsbach in 1893 of the gas mantle impregnated with thorium oxide created a considerable demand for thorium, but this subsequently declined, owing to competition from improved electric lamps. The new demand for nuclear fuel has revived the interest in thorium.

The pure metal tarnishes in the air when freshly cut, and is easily scratched with a knife. Its density is less than that of uranium, and about the same as that of lead. Its variations in crystalline form are much less complicated than those of uranium, and it does not go through extreme changes in shape. It can be extensively cold-worked without annealing, and the associated heat treatment is only of minor importance. Objects can be fabricated from it by powder metallurgy. It is, however, chemically reactive and has a high melting-point, 1,750° C. These properties make smelting difficult. The metal reacts at this high temperature with nearly every kind of crucible lining. The most satisfactory is beryllium oxide. The charge is heated by electric induction in an atmosphere of helium or argon in a furnace. There is much scope for the development of thorium smelting on an industrial scale.

The valuable nuclear properties of beryllium have greatly increased attention to this metal. It is obtained from the mineral beryl, which exists in large quantities in low-grade deposits. Beryllium is an excellent moderator of neutrons in nuclear reactors. It is practically unaffected by intense irradiation in reactor cores. In addition to this, it is quite resistant to corrosion by air and by water, nor is it attacked by liquid sodium at 500° C. It melts at about 1,100° C. Its oxide is also an excellent neutron moderator.

Unfortunately, however, the pure metal, and its oxide, are extraordinarily brittle. During the last quarter of a century a considerable amount of beryllium has been used in alloys. A small amount enormously increases the quality of bronze springs, which are much used in electrical equipment such as telephones. But in spite of much effort, very few uses were found for pure beryllium metal, because of the extreme difficulty of working it.

Since the release of atomic energy, most determined efforts have been made to overcome this problem, with considerable success. Studies of beryllium crystals have shown that the brittleness is due to breaking along one of the crystal planes, while along another, slip is very easy. By giving beryllium sheet appropriate treatment, its constituent crystals can be aligned so that their planes of easy slip are parallel with that of the sheet. When this has been done, the sheet becomes extremely ductile along its length.

In the United States, beryllium metal is made by the reduction of beryllium fluoride with magnesium metal. This produces a solid block, consisting of pebbles of the metal embedded in slag. The pebbles are extracted and melted in a vacuum. Various impurities are distilled off, and the molten metal is cast in ingots of about 70 lb. weight.

Not much, except extrusion, can be done with the ingots as such, as they are exceedingly brittle. They machine very poorly, owing to the extreme variation of strength in different directions of the constituent crystals. Consequently, the ingots are reduced to powder, which has been handled more successfully by the methods of powder metallurgy. But the successful production of beryllium castings with a fine grain, which could be satisfactorily machined, would be of great economic value, as castings are much cheaper than the products of powder metallurgy.

Beryllium sticks to dies, so it is encased in steel, and the whole extruded at temperatures of about 1,000° C. Round bars and flat shapes are made by this method. Beryllium powder encased in a steel container can be rolled and forged.

Small parts are made by pressing cold powder at pressures of up to 100 tons per square inch, sintering at about 1,100° C., and rolled or extruded at about 450° C.

Thin tubes and rods of irregular cross-section are made by low-pressure treatment of powder in steel moulds at temperatures of about 1,050° C.

Beryllium parts fabricated from powder can be far more ductile than the cast metal because its constituent grains are very much smaller. For the same reason, beryllium made by the powder process machines far more satisfactorily than castings. Unfortunately, there are further difficulties. The metal is very abrasive, and wears down tools. Finally, beryllium dust is very dangerous to the health, being particularly liable to cause diseases of the lungs, so stringent precautions have to be taken against it.

Beryllium is both a very promising and a very difficult metal. It has been partially mastered only by the most determined efforts. But its qualities, and the advances in treatment, are such that it is safely predicted that the beryllium industry will grow very considerably during the next ten or twenty years.

Zirconium is another metal which has been brought by nuclear engineering into the industrial field. It was discovered by Klaproth in 1789, but such is the difficulty of preparing the pure metal that this was not achieved even in the laboratory until 1925.

Zirconium is very transparent to slow-speed neutrons, and it is almost the best metal in general resistance to all forms of corrosion.

Besides resisting many chemical corrosives, zirconium is completely resistant to sea-water. This is important in nuclear reactors for ships, and zirconium has in fact been extensively used in the power plant of the U.S. submarine *Nautilus*. It is completely resistant, too, to hydrazine, an organic compound used, among other applications, as a propellant in rockets.

In addition to its neutron transparency and resistance to corrosion, it has good mechanical properties and good fabricating qualities.

For these reasons, it is the best material for encasing or cladding the fuel elements of reactors.

As the extraction of zirconium is so difficult, the metal was regarded as rare, but it is actually more plentiful than nickel, copper, lead or zinc. Tens of millions of tons of zirconium ore have been located. In 1945 the U.S. Bureau of Mines attacked the problem of producing it on an industrial scale. Under the technical direction of W. J. Kroll, who had formerly perfected the process for preparing titanium by reducing titanium tetrachloride with magnesium in inert helium gas, a similar method for preparing zirconium was successfully found. By January 1955 the U.S. Bureau of Mines had produced 1,112,000 lb. of the metal, at an average cost of $9·33 per lb.

One of the difficulties in refining zirconium is that in the molten state it becomes an almost universal solvent, and acquires impurities very easily.

Another difficulty is that it occurs in nature in association with the rare element hafnium, to which it is chemically very closely related. Unfortunately, hafnium is one of the strongest absorbers of neutrons, so a small amount of hafnium impurity in zirconium spoils its most valuable quality of transparency to neutrons. The separation of hafnium and zirconium, which was formerly extremely difficult, is now elegantly performed by counter-current chemical exchange methods.

Hafnium, whose very existence was forecast only from recondite quantum theory, was not found in nature until 1920, and now it is becoming of industrial use as a neutron absorber in the control rods of nuclear reactors.

Apart from metals which were hitherto not used, there are the entirely new metallic elements synthetized in nuclear reactors. The most important of these, so far, is plutonium. The methods of preparing and fabricating it have been worked out in only fifteen years, since it was discovered in 1940.

Then there are the other new synthetic elements: Neptunium, Americium, Curium, Berkelium, Californium, Einsteinium, Fermium and Mendeleevium. All of these have their chemistries and metallurgies, and no doubt in due course will have their industrial uses.

One of the non-metallic materials in which nuclear energy has raised new interest is graphite. It was used in the earliest reactors because it was the most readily available moderator of neutrons. It is relatively inexpensive, and can be machined more easily than any metal.

Fresh interest in graphite is arising from its excellence as a refractory material at high temperatures, and its resistance to liquid metals. For instance, it is completely unaffected by liquid tin and liquid bismuth at 1,500° C. It may therefore have an important rôle in the construction of liquid metal cooled nuclear reactors.

Graphite is also very transparent to neutrons. A slow neutron has a path of more than 30 metres in graphite before it is absorbed. In the future, economy in the utilization of neutrons will be a dominant factor in the design of efficient nuclear power plants, for it leads to economy in the fissile material from which they are obtained. The excellence of graphite in this respect, combined with its other qualities, will attract the most serious consideration in the design of high-temperature industrial nuclear power plants, which should be economical both in construction and in the consumption of neutrons.

Graphite is unique as a material of construction, for in some ways it resembles both metals and ceramics. It conducts heat and electricity well, but it lacks ductility and cannot be melted, cast, rolled, forged or welded. As it expands little with heat, and has considerable strength at high temperature, it is the most resistant of all materials to sudden big changes in temperature.

Its most serious limitations are that it oxidizes at high temperatures, and is permeable to gases and liquids. Research is showing how these qualities can be modified, and graphite pipes have already been made which are impervious to liquids and gases at moderate pressures. It is expected that graphite pipes for transporting liquid metal cooling media in reactors will soon be successfully produced. It is expected, too, that ways of coating the graphite so that it will resist oxidation will also be found.

Artificial graphite is manufactured by the process introduced by E. G. Acheson in 1895. Petroleum or coal is made into a plastic mixture which can be moulded into rods or tubes, or other desired shapes. These are fired in an electric furnace at 3,000° C.

For producing very pure graphite for use in nuclear reactors, the material is purified by heating it with an electric current to a temperature of 2,500° C. in an atmosphere of a gas which combines with the impurities. The product is so pure that it is easier to measure its purity by testing it in a nuclear reactor for testing materials, than by chemical analysis. It contains less than 20 parts per million of impurities.

The turning of the coke plastic into graphite by baking at high temperature produces a fall of electrical resistance by a factor of 5, an increase of heat conductivity by a factor of 25, a 50 per cent decrease in expansion under heat, and a 20 per cent decrease in elasticity and strength. When the graphite is exposed to irradiation by neutrons in a reactor, these qualities change back in the reverse direction.

It seems that the effect is not influenced by the intensity of the stream or flux of neutrons. It makes the graphite stronger, harder and more brittle. It breaks up the crystal structure of the graphite and turns it back into an amorphous material. When the graphite is kept in a nuclear reactor at low temperature, its mechanical strength may be doubled, and its heat conductivity reduced by a factor of 50. It may expand more than 3 per cent. By annealing treatment at 2,000° C., however, the qualities of the graphite can be substantially restored.

Investigations into the explanation of radiation damage to graphite and metals is throwing light on the principles underlying the properties of solid bodies, and some authorities believe that this work may prove to be one of the most important results of the development of nuclear energy, inspiring fundamental advances in the knowledge of engineering materials and leading to new and improved materials, and methods of working them.

The best moderator is heavy water, which consists of molecules containing atoms of heavy hydrogen, which are twice as heavy as atoms of ordinary hydrogen. A measure of the quality of a moderator, particularly for use near natural uranium, is the ratio of its power to slow down neutrons to its power of absorbing them. For heavy water this ratio is 5,000, compared with 202 for graphite, 145 for beryllium and 62 for ordinary water. The excellence of heavy water as a moderator is due to the transfer by collision of the energy of the neutrons to the nuclei of heavy hydrogen, or deuterons, in the heavy water.

Owing to its exceptional value as a moderator, heavy water, though it was discovered only in 1932, is now produced on an industrial scale. Unfortunately, its production is difficult, so it is very expensive. In August 1955 the U.S. Atomic Energy Commission announced that it would sell heavy water, on certain terms, at a price of $28 per lb., or about £22,000 per ton. This is an exceptionally low price, but it is sufficient to indicate the cost of heavy water. A nuclear reactor, using heavy water as moderator, and in some cases also as cooling medium, would require from 5 to 200 tons of the material; 1,000 to 5,000 kilowatts of electricity can be obtained from a power reactor per ton of heavy water used.

Ordinary water contains about 1 part in 6,000 of heavy water. As the amount of water on the earth is very large, heavy water is not rare, but it is not easily separated from ordinary water. The separation depends on slight differences in behaviour of ordinary hydrogen and heavy hydrogen. When water is decomposed by an electric current, the amount of heavy hydrogen in the hydrogen released at the cathode is lower than that in the remaining water. Heavy water was first produced on a considerable industrial scale at the hydro-electric power plant at Rjukan in Norway, where large quantities of hydrogen were produced by electrolysis for the synthetic ammonia industry. The plant used about 100,000 kilowatts of electricity, and it produced 1·7 tons of heavy water per year as a by-product.

Unless several tons per year of heavy water are produced for at least ten years, it does not pay to build a plant to produce heavy water alone. It is more economic to produce it as a by-product of synthetic ammonia production, in which large quantities of hydrogen are available. But the biggest synthetic ammonia plants would not produce enough spare hydrogen to make more than 40 tons of heavy water a year, which is not enough for supplying a nuclear power industry in which a single big reactor might require 200 tons of heavy water. Consequently, special plants are necessary.

The three processes which appear to be best suited for large-scale production are distillation, electrolysis of water, and chemical exchange. There are many ways of carrying out each of these, but the choice in any particular case will depend on local conditions and resources. In countries where electricity is plentiful and cheap, such as Canada and Norway, electrolysis may be preferred.

In France, a contract has been placed for the production of heavy hydrogen by distillation of liquid hydrogen, the hydrogen for liquefaction being supplied by a synthetic ammonia plant. This process is theoretically very efficient, but the handling of large quantities of liquid hydrogen on the industrial scale is technically difficult.

When ordinary water is distilled, the molecules containing ordinary hydrogen evaporate slightly quicker than those containing heavy hydrogen. By arranging a sequence of distillations, substantial quantities of heavy hydrogen can be separated. Much steam is required, and where it is cheap the process is attractive. British and New Zealand scientists and engineers have proposed to utilize this principle for producing heavy water and electric power in a combined plant from the large quantities of volcanic steam escaping from the ground in the North Island of New Zealand. The steam would be sent up towers packed with porous metal which provides a very large area for condensation, and thereby speeds up the separation.

The need for removing the intense heat from the core of nuclear reactors has stimulated much research on the use of liquid metals for cooling. Hitherto, this technique has not been much used in heavy engineering, though it has been widely adopted for cooling the valves of aircraft engines.

The most suitable metals for liquid cooling are sodium and

potassium. Both of them melt below the boiling-point of water. An alloy of the two metals melts at − 11° C., and is therefore liquid at room temperatures. Both metals boil only at the fairly high temperatures of 780°–880° C.

As is well known, sodium and potassium decompose water at room temperatures, and are very reactive chemically. For these reasons it had been believed that they were fundamentally too dangerous and difficult for use on a large technological scale. But thorough research has shown that this is not so. They do not corrode uranium, and it has been discovered that if they are carefully purified, they do not corrode steels resistant to high temperatures.

As the metals are chemical elements, and not chemical compounds, such, for example, as water, they cannot be decomposed chemically by heat or radiation. As metals, they conduct heat comparatively well, and consequently are able to transfer heat at a high rate. This enables them to remove the heat from a reactor core without being driven through very rapidly. Liquid metal cooling can be carried out successfully at pressures of 50–150 lb. per square inch, compared with pressures of 1,000–2,000 lb. per square inch for water cooling, thus greatly simplifying problems of mechanical design.

Sodium and potassium do not absorb neutrons unduly, but as they are not good moderators for slowing down neutrons, they are best utilized in fast reactors.

When sodium and potassium pass through the reactor core, they become very radioactive, so it is necessary to guard against the escape of cooling media which are radioactive as well as inflammable. Consequently, the cooling system must be particularly proof against leaks. Joints are fusion-welded, or brazed with a nickel-manganese compound. The system may be enclosed in a blanket of inert gas, such as helium, to prevent air from leaking in.

The Experimental Breeder Reactor at the Argonne National Laboratory in the U.S. has worked successfully with a liquid metal cooling system for more than four years.

As the avoidance of leaks is of great importance, the pumping of liquid metal has been a primary problem. It is best done with the electro-magnetic pump. This takes advantage of the comparatively high electrical conductivity of the liquid metals. If a stream of liquid metal has a strong electric current sent through it, then it will react to a magnetic field in the same way as if it were an ordinary wire carrying the same current. It will experience a force which will push it in a certain direction, exactly as in the wires of an electric motor. Hence the engineer can arrange that the liquid metal is pushed or pumped along a pipe, by the force from a magnet out side the pipe. The liquid metal can be moved along without

FIG. 99.—A FLAT LINEAR ELECTRO-MAGNETIC INDUCTION PUMP.
(*The English Electric Company Ltd.*

touching it, and the problem of joints and valves is very much simplified.

Electro-magnetic pumps, like electric motors, will work on direct or on alternating current. In the latter case, they are of the induction type, and will run off the ordinary electricity supply. Fig. 99 shows such a pump working at 120 lb. per square inch.

The development of a nuclear power industry will produce radioactive fission products on a large scale, and the cost of utilization or disposal of these products will be an important item in the future economics of nuclear power. The comparatively small amounts of radioactive wastes produced at present are usually stored in underground steel-lined tanks. The capital cost of constructing these tanks is up to $2 per gallon. The radioactivity produces a great deal of heat which must be removed by a cooling system. It is not known how long these tanks will last. The surrounding ground is monitored, in order to detect any leakage of the radioactive materials.

When the radioactivity of the wastes has decayed to a low value, the residue is incorporated in containers and buried in the ground or dumped into the sea. According to Wolman and Gorman, the cost of land burial is about \$0·14–\$2·00 per cubic foot, and sea-burial about \$10 per cubic foot. The high cost of sea-burial is due to the expense of transporting material which must be heavily shielded.

Oceanographers are much concerned about the effects of dumping of fission wastes into the ocean. It has been suggested that these should be dumped into the very deep canyons or fissures which exist on the edge of the continental shelf in various oceans. But it appears that the bottoms of these canyons are scoured by water currents moving at from 15 to 50 miles per hour. The impact of the container on the hard bottom and the jostling by these fierce currents might break the container and disperse its contents. Possibly the dumping of fission wastes into the ocean is less likely to lead to hazards if they are dumped over the edge of the continental shelf.

Much remains to be learned of how the radioactive fission products will affect marine life. It is known that certain plankton can extract particular radioactive substances from the water and thereby increase the radioactivity in themselves by a factor of 1,000. As fish feed on plankton, and men feed on fish, it is necessary to ascertain with certainty that the method of disposing of radioactive wastes will not involve this and other hazards.

In the U.K. Atomic Energy Authority's plant at Windscale, radioactive wastes of low intensity are discharged into the Irish Sea. The radioactive effects on marine organisms have been carefully observed, and, so far, observations on local fish have not shown that they have become dangerously radioactive. Sea-weed seems to absorb somewhat more radioactivity than fish.

However, every aspect of radioactive dispersal requires very thorough investigation. It has been found that the leaves of deciduous trees growing near nuclear energy plants concentrate radioactivity. As the leaves fall in the autumn, they may disperse these concentrations of radioactivity over the neighbourhood. Consequently, in some cases, woods near nuclear energy plants have already been cut down.

The best method of safely disposing of the products of nuclear fission is to find a use for them, especially the most dangerous ones, such as strontium 90 and caesium 137. These are already used in isotope applications, as mentioned on page 126. Research will undoubtedly discover further uses for these and other constituents of what is at present radioactive waste.

The fission products also provide an immense store of radioactive

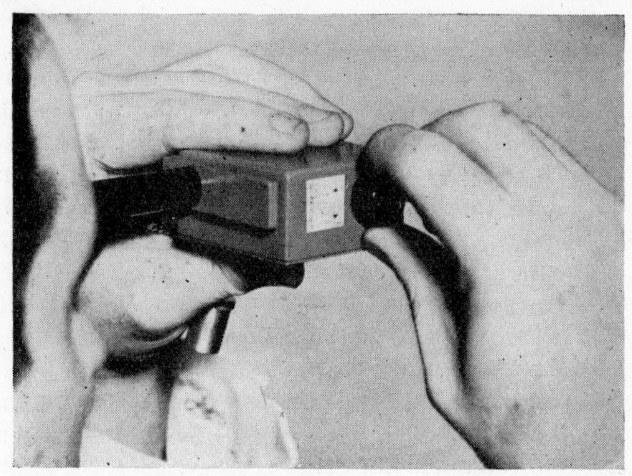

FIG. 100.—A DOSIMETER OPERATED BY AN ELECTRIC CURRENT PRODUCED BY AN ATOMIC BATTERY.

(Radiation Research Corporation)

radiation, for which uses are being sought. It is found that radiation can produce cross-linking effects in certain polymer plastics. This converts them into tough materials which will not melt. In others, it breaks the main-chain, changing the plastics from a solid into a viscous liquid. These discoveries are the first steps in the development of a new branch of chemical industry.

One of the most elegant ways of utilizing radioactive radiation is to convert it directly into electrical energy. Indeed, the direct conversion of nuclear energy into electrical energy, without the complicated interposition of steam turbogenerator plants, is one of the main aims of nuclear energy development.

Direct conversion of radioactive radiation into electrical energy was observed by Pierre and Marie Curie in 1900, but has only recently been developed into a practical process. So far, it is only on a very small, though quite useful scale. The total amount of energy in the radiation from fission products is a very small fraction of the amount of energy released during the production of these fission products. Nevertheless, a considerable amount of power could be obtained from them, if the nuclear energy industry were big enough to supply them in sufficient quantity.

Several principles have been employed in the various direct conversion devices which have already been made. One of these consists of a plastic insulator which allows fast electrons from a strontium 90 source to pass through it, but does not allow low-energy particles to pass in the reverse direction. The fast electrons are picked up on an electrode, and drawn off as a current of very low amperage, but high voltage. Fig. 100 illustrates a dosimeter operated by an atomic battery of this type.

Much interest has recently been shown in devices utilizing semi-conductors, such as silicon or germanium. A junction is made out of two types of silicon, the *p* and the *n* types. In the region of this junction there is an internal electric field. Radiations from a radio-isotope, such as strontium 90, are directed at the silicon. They produce in it pairs of particles, one negatively and one positively charged. The pairs of particles diffuse through the silicon towards the joints, where the internal electric field sorts the particles out, sending the negatives in one direction and the positives in the opposite, thus setting up an electric current.

Such semi-conductor batteries convert 3 per cent of the radiation energy into electrical energy, and their efficiency rises with power. The present limit is due to irradiation damage, but it is expected that research will show how this may be reduced. The Bell Telephone Company is now producing commercially a silicon semi-conductor cell, which converts up to 11 per cent of solar radiation falling on it into electric current. These cells are at present expensive, costing 25 dollars per square inch, but batteries of them are already used for charging accumulators in telephone systems and for operating portable radio transmitters and receivers.

The use of the radioisotope nickel 63, which emits radiation of low energy, might be more suitable, but it is very expensive. If special attention were given to the reduction of the cost of its extraction from fission products, a big advance in the utilization of atomic batteries might be made.

Among the applications already in sight are meters for measuring radiation, dosimeters for measuring doses of radiation, chargers for condensers, compensators for restoring leakage from electrical instruments, and voltage sources which can be used as standards for reference.

Since the discovery of radioactivity in 1896, investigation into its nature and applications has advanced at an ever-increasing pace. At every stage, advance has been swifter than was forecast by the leading authorities, and especially since the discovery of nuclear fission in 1938. It is to be expected, then, that the utilization of nuclear energy in industry will develop more quickly, and in more directions, than even the most penetrating scientists and engineers can foresee at present.

INDEX